Bond
No.1 for exam success

D1549247

Verbal Reasoning

Assessment Papers

9–10 years

Book 1

OXFORD
UNIVERSITY PRESS

OXFORD
UNIVERSITY PRESS

Great Clarendon Street, Oxford, OX2 6DP, United Kingdom

Oxford University Press is a department of the University of Oxford.
It furthers the University's objective of excellence in research,
scholarship, and education by publishing worldwide. Oxford is
a registered trade mark of Oxford University Press in the UK and in
certain other countries

British Library Cataloguing in Publication Data
Data available

978-0-19-274033-5

10 9 8 7 6 5

Paper used in the production of this book is a natural, recyclable
product made from wood grown in sustainable forests.
The manufacturing process conforms to the environmental
regulations of the country of origin.

Printed in China

Acknowledgements

The publishers would like to thank the following for permissions to
use copyright material:

Page make-up: OKS Prepress, India
Cover illustrations: Lo Cole

Although we have made every effort to trace and contact all
copyright holders before publication this has not been possible in all
cases. If notified, the publisher will rectify any errors or omissions at
the earliest opportunity.

Links to third party websites are provided by Oxford in good faith
and for information only. Oxford disclaims any responsibility for
the materials contained in any third party website referenced in
this work.

Before you get started

What is Bond?

This book is part of the Bond Assessment Papers series for verbal reasoning, which provides a **thorough and progressive course in verbal reasoning** from ages six to twelve. It builds up reasoning skills from book to book over the course of the series.

What does this book cover and how can it be used to prepare for exams?

Verbal reasoning questions can be grouped into four distinct groups: sorting words, selecting words, anagrams, coded sequences and logic. *Verbal Reasoning 9–10 Book 1 and Book 2* practise a wide range of questions appropriate to the age group drawn from all these categories. The papers can be used both for general practice and as part of the run-up to 11+ and other selective exams. One of the key features of Bond Assessment Papers is that each one practises **a very wide variety of skills and question types** so that children are always challenged to think – and don't get bored repeating the same question type again and again. We believe that variety is the key to effective learning. It helps children 'think on their feet' and cope with the unexpected: it is surprising how often children come out of verbal reasoning exams having met question types they have not seen before.

What does this book contain?

- **15 papers** – each one contains 65 questions.
- **Tutorial links throughout** – [📖] – this icon appears in the margin next to the questions. It indicates links to the relevant section in *How to do 11+ Verbal Reasoning*, our invaluable subject guide that offers explanations and practice for all core question types.
- **Scoring devices** – there are score boxes in the margins and a Progress Chart on page 60. The chart is a visual and motivating way for children to see how they are doing. It also turns the score into a percentage that can help decide what to do next.
- **Next Steps Planner** – advice on what to do after finishing the papers can be found on the inside back cover.
- **Answers** – located in an easily-removed central pull-out section.

How can you use this book?

One of the great strengths of Bond Assessment Papers is their flexibility. They can be used at home, in school and by tutors to:
- set **timed formal practice** tests – allow about 40 minutes per paper. Reduce the suggested time limit by five minutes to practise working at speed.
- provide **bite-sized chunks** for regular practice
- **highlight strengths and weaknesses** in the core skills
- identify **individual needs**
- set **homework**
- follow a **complete 11+ preparation strategy** alongside *The Parents' Guide to the 11+* (see overleaf).

It is best to start at the beginning and work though the papers in order. If you are using the book as part of a careful run-in to the 11+, we suggest that you also have two other essential Bond resources close at hand:

How to do 11+ Verbal Reasoning: the subject guide that explains all the question types practised in this book. Use the cross-reference icons to find the relevant sections.

The Parents' Guide to the 11+: the step-by-step guide to the whole 11+ experience. It clearly explains the 11+ process, provides guidance on how to assess children, helps you to set complete action plans for practice and explains how you can use *Verbal Reasoning 9–10 Book 1 and Book 2* as part of a strategic run-in to the exam.

See the inside front cover for more details of these books.

What does a score mean and how can it be improved?

It is unfortunately impossible to predict how a child will perform when it comes to the 11+ (or similar) exam if they achieve a certain score on any practice book or paper. Success on the day depends on a host of factors, including the scores of the other children sitting the test. However, we can give some guidance on what a score indicates and how to improve it.

If children colour in the Progress Chart on page 60, this will give an idea of present performance in percentage terms. The Next Steps Planner inside the back cover will help you to decide what to do next to help a child progress. It is always valuable to go over wrong answers with children. If they are having trouble with any particular question type, follow the tutorial links to *How to do 11+ Verbal Reasoning* for step-by-step explanations and further practice.

Don't forget the website...!

Visit www.bond11plus.co.uk for lots of advice, information and suggestions on everything to do with Bond, the 11+ and helping children to do their best, and exams.

Paper 1

Underline the pair of words most similar in meaning.

> **Example**   come, go   <u>roam, wander</u>   fear, fare

1 fly, wing   easy, simple   under, over

2 go, depart   quarrel, agree   write, read

3 narrow, broad   plain, decorated   new, fresh

4 night, day   collect, distribute   tired, weary

5 hide, conceal   rush, delay   jump, walk

Underline the two words, one from each group, which are most opposite in meaning.

> **Example**   (dawn, <u>early</u>, wake)   (<u>late</u>, stop, sunrise)

6 (sell, make, use)   (study, purchase, remove)

7 (dim, weak, sturdy)   (bright, mild, blurry)

8 (long, far, back)   (distance, front, length)

9 (lesson, question, talk)   (report, teacher, answer)

10 (accept, advance, aware)   (refuse, alive, rubbish)

Complete the following sentences by selecting the most sensible word from each group of words given in the brackets. Underline the words selected.

> **Example**   The (<u>children</u>, books, foxes) carried the (houses, <u>books</u>, steps) home
> from the (greengrocer, <u>library</u>, factory).

11 The (farmer, sailor, boy) was going to the (docks, shed, swimming pool) to (shop, milk the cows, read a book).

12 Ann took her (spoon, spade, hoe) to the (garden, beach, park) as she wanted to build a (bridge, castle, palace).

13 Don't (put, lose, forget) to (find, eat, post) this (stamp, sock, letter).

14 The (plane, porter, eagle) carried the (sea, suitcase, food) to its (runway, nest, ground).

15 The (television, friend, lantern) lit his (face, knee, elbow), as he (ran, threw, buried) the treasure.

Underline the two words which are made from the same letters.

> **Example**   TAP   PET   <u>TEA</u>   POT   <u>EAT</u>

16 PIANO   PLATE   PLAYS   PEDAL   PETAL

17 SHALL   HOUSE   SHORE   HOMES   HORSE

1

18 CHAIR	CHEST	TABLE	BLAME	BLEAT
19 BEACH	BENCH	BOUGH	HEADS	SHADE
20 LEAST	PLEAT	LATER	STALE	TABLE

B 21

Write the four-letter word hidden at the end of one word and the beginning of the next word. The order of the letters may not be changed.

Example The children had bats and balls. *sand*

21 This book can be very useful. _____

22 The rough lad was very strong. _____

23 There are fairies at the bottom of the garden. _____

24 This house is often cold. _____

25 Will the journey end soon? _____

B 10

Find the letter which will end the first word and start the second word.

Example peac (h) ome

26 mad (___) rror   27 ris (___) ing   28 lis (___) hen

29 til (___) eave   30 foo (___) rade

B 17

Find and underline the two words which need to change places for each sentence to make sense.

Example She went to <u>letter</u> the <u>write</u>.

31 How do you today feel?

32 As tights is cold I am wearing it.

33 I like hairdo new your.

34 I'm sorry glass broken the I've.

35 I'll home to get him have.

B 23

Fill in the missing letters and numbers. The alphabet has been written out to help you.

Example AB is to CD as PQ is to *RS* .

A B C D E F G H I J K L M N O P Q R S T U V W X Y Z

36 AB is to CD as EF is to _____.

37 AC is to DF as GI is to _____.

38 M2 is to N4 as O6 is to _____.

39 9BC is to 12BC as 15BC is to _____.

40 8AB is to 6BC as 4CD is to _____.

Which one letter can be added to the front of all of these words to make new words?

B 12

Example _c_are   _c_at   _c_rate   _c_all

41 ___ate   ___ear   ___our   ___ist

42 ___harp   ___lender   ___hut   ___lit

43 ___edge   ___asp   ___allow   ___hole

44 ___ace   ___aid   ___age   ___ale

45 ___ate   ___ream   ___angle   ___rove

5

Fill in the crosswords so that all the given words are included. You have been given one letter as a clue in each crossword.

B 19

46
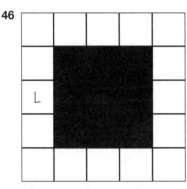
charm, moles, music, storm

47
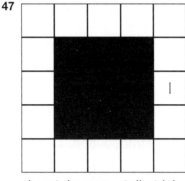
heart, humps, stalk, trick

48

edits, knife, knits, knock

49

films, finer, fluff, rages

50

poles, pound, plump, stand

5

If the code for PROTECT is £ ! : * ? / *, what are the codes for the following words?

51 TORE   **52** PORT   **53** CROP

_____   _____   _____

3

If the code for PLANTER is ÷ = + : − % ×, what do the following codes stand for?

54 −×+÷   **55** ×%+=

_____   _____

2

Choose the word or phrase that makes each sentence true.

Example   A LIBRARY always has (posters, a carpet, <u>books</u>, DVDs, stairs).

56 A BIRD always has a (nest, beak, chick, worm, twig).

57 A PLANT always has (flowers, berries, roots, branches, a pot).

58 A SHOE always has a (strap, button, sole, zipper, foot).

59 A HOUSE always has (bricks, walls, a drive, a garden, a doorbell).

60 A COAT always has (buttons, pockets, sleeves, a belt, a zipper).

5

Remove two letters from the word in capital letters to leave a new word. The meaning of the new word is given in the clue.

Example   MONKEY   lives in a monastery   <u>monk</u>

61 STREET   type of plant   _____

62 LEARNT   tilt   _____

63 STRAND   on a beach   _____

64 FRAMES   renown   _____

65 SPRAIN   twirl   _____

5

Paper 2

Underline the two words in each line which are most similar in type or meaning.

Example   <u>dear</u>   pleasant   poor   extravagant   <u>expensive</u>

1 alter	after	sound	fond	change
2 form	frozen	fear	fell	fright
3 sit	fidget	stand	wriggle	kick
4 ready	right	hard	simple	difficult
5 start	end	lend	begin	borrow

Underline the pair of words most opposite in meaning.

Example   cup, mug   coffee, milk   <u>hot, cold</u>

6 circle, round	shiny, dull	enemy, foe
7 pause, rest	generous, mean	angry, cross
8 home, away	bridge, river	yours, his
9 often, seldom	great, big	speak, talk
10 tug, pull	raise, lower	push, shove

Underline two words, one from each group, that go together to form a new word. The word in the first group always comes first.

Example   (hand, <u>green</u>, for)   (light, <u>house</u>, sure)

11 (name, pay, try)   (less, use, more)

12 (keep, look, out)   (safe, sane, sake)

13 (on, be, in)   (head, wind, shoulders)

14 (chapter, page, text)   (book, mark, word)

15 (cub, key, money)   (board, lock, safe)

Find the three-letter word which can be added to the letters in capitals to make a new word. The new word will complete the sentence sensibly.

Example   The cat sprang onto the MO. <u>USE</u>

16 The thief was arrested for SLING a car.   _____

17 The grandmother thought that the children had GN quite a bit since she'd last seen them.   _____

18 The class went to the THRE to see a pantomime.   _____

19 Dad WED the food up in the oven because we were late for lunch.   _____

20 The woman put the flowers she had just picked in a BET.   _____

5

Write the four-letter word hidden at the end of one word and the beginning of the next word. The order of the letters may not be changed.

B 21

Example   The children had bats and balls.   _sand_

21 This candle is very pretty.   _____

22 You must learn the alphabet.   _____

23 My grandmother bakes delicious cakes.   _____

24 The strong wind took the kite miles away.   _____

25 He drove the car in the mud.   _____

5

Change the first word into the last word, by changing one letter at a time and making a new, different word in the middle.

B 13

Example   CASE _CASH_ LASH

26 SEND _____ SANG   27 CAKE _____ MALE

28 DEAR _____ MEAL   29 CALL _____ BAIL

30 HOME _____ COMB

5

Complete the following sentences by selecting the most sensible word from each group of words given in the brackets. Underline the words selected.

B 14

Example   The (children, books, foxes) carried the (houses, books, steps) home from the (greengrocer, library, factory).

31 The (sheep, lions, dogs) were in a (town, field, shop) grazing the (bones, grass, chicken) contentedly.

32 The (dog, otter, tiger) paced back and forth in the (jungle, cage, field) at the (farm, zoo, park).

33 Under a (stone, book, kitchen) there lived a (house, pond, frog) who ate (dogs, porridge, flies).

34 The (new, fast, old) car crept slowly (through, along, up) the (sunny, flat, steep) hill.

35 Don't (swim, eat, move)! There's a (pig, coat, snake) on that (shelf, sun, rock).

5

Choose two words, one from each set of brackets, to complete the sentences in the best way.

B 15

Example   Smile is to happiness as (drink, tear, shout) is to (whisper, laugh, sorrow).

36 Tuesday is to Wednesday as (May, March, April) is to (March, May, July).

37 Puppy is to dog as (cat, lamb, ewe) is to (dog, sheep, pig).

38 Author is to book as (man, sculptor, artist) is to (picture, paint, woman).

39 Plate is to eat as (knife, cup, watch) is to (drink, fork, saucer).

40 Aunt is to niece as (mother, uncle, nephew) is to (nephew, boy, sister).

5

Fill in the crosswords so that all the given words are included. You have been given one letter as a clue in each crossword.

41

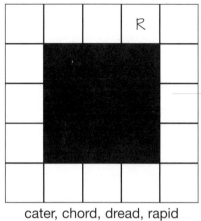

cater, chord, dread, rapid

42

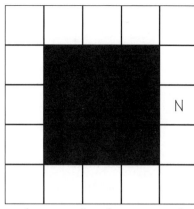

dance, sails, shave, sound

43

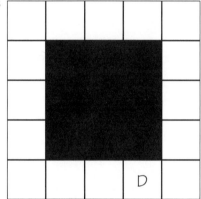

handy, harsh, human, nasty

44

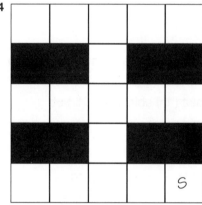

curse, eases, ropes, taper

45

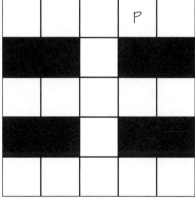

camps, mouth, other, truce

5

Give the missing numbers in the following sequences.

Example   2   4   6   8   <u>10</u>   <u>12</u>

46 91   ____   73   64   ____   46

47 ____ $\frac{3}{4}$ ____ $1\frac{1}{4}$ $1\frac{1}{2}$ $1\frac{3}{4}$

48 70   ____   ____   49   42   35

49 66   77   88   ____   ____   121

50 1   2   4   5   ____   ____

B 23

5

Here are the codes for four words. Match the right word to the right code.

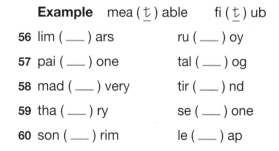

MAN   AND   MEN   AN

51 MAN _____   52 AND _____

53 MEN _____   54 AN _____

55 Using the same code, encode MEND. _____

B 24

5

Find the letter which will complete both pairs of words, ending the first word and starting the second. The same letter must be used for both pairs of words.

Example   mea (<u>t</u>) able   fi (<u>t</u>) ub

56 lim (___) ars   ru (___) oy

57 pai (___) one   tal (___) og

58 mad (___) very   tir (___) nd

59 tha (___) ry   se (___) one

60 son (___) rim   le (___) ap

B 10

5

Rearrange the letters in capitals to make another word. The new word has something to do with the first two words.

Example   spot   soil   SAINT   <u>STAIN</u>

61 pain   throb   EACH   _____

62 start   commence   BEING   _____

63 beneath   lower   ELBOW   _____

64 inexpensive   economical   PEACH   _____

65 man   boy   MEAL   _____

B 16

5

Paper 3

Underline the word in the brackets that goes best with the words given outside the brackets.

B 5

Example   word, paragraph, sentence   (pen, cap, <u>letter</u>, top, stop)

1 sleet, snow, rain   (sunny, hot, frost, cool, hail)

2 sty, lair, hutch   (flat, bungalow, hotel, cottage, stable)

3 sprouts, beans, swede   (oranges, plums, blackberries, carrots, limes)

4 talk, chatter, utter   (cough, speak, blow, splutter, sneeze)

5 children, tots, infants   (age, school, toddlers, adults, grannies)

5

Underline the two words, one from each group, which are the most opposite in meaning.

B 9

Example   (dawn, <u>early</u>, wake)   (<u>late</u>, stop, sunrise)

6 (money, spend, purse)   (cash, notes, save)

7 (equal, same, mend)   (similar, different, cheap)

8 (join, quit, try)   (wait, start, consider)

9 (crowded, alone, lonely)   (deserted, earned, bought)

10 (wrestle, fight, hurt)   (heal, war, wrong)

5

Find the letter which will end the first word and start the second word.

B 10

Example   peac (<u>h</u>) ome

11 tim (___) ast   12 sea (___) ray

13 men (___) iet   14 spea (___) est

15 bal (___) and

5

Find a word that can be put in front of each of the following words to make new, compound words.

B 11

Example   cast   fall   ward   pour   _down_

16 ball   step   print   path   _____

17 stairs   set   right   turn   _____

18 mark   shelf   keeper   worm   _____

19 side   form   hale   put   _____

20 scarf   lock   light   quarters   _____

5

9

Write the four-letter word hidden at the end of one word and the beginning of the next word. The order of the letters may not be changed.

Example   The children had bats and balls.   <u>sand</u>

21 These curtains are too long.   _____

22 The time shows it is quite late.   _____

23 I like the sea and the mountains.   _____

24 She admitted her homework was very late.   _____

25 The apple tree was in the back garden.   _____

Find and underline the two words which need to change places for the sentence to make sense.

Example   She went to <u>letter</u> the <u>write</u>.

26 The leg of the broken was chair.

27 Have enough got you?

28 Untidy writing is very my.

29 What now you want do?

30 Cup make another I'll of tea.

Give the missing numbers in the following sequences.

Example   2   4   6   8   <u>10</u>   <u>12</u>

31 ___   59   67   75   ___   91

32 105   ___   ___   45   25   5

33 ___   96   84   72   ___   48

34 46   42   38   ___   30   ___

35 15   20   21   26   ___   ___

Fill in the crosswords so that all the given words are included. You have been given one letter as a clue in each crossword.

36

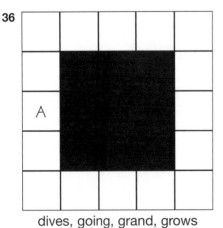

dives, going, grand, grows

37

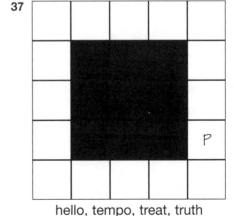

hello, tempo, treat, truth

38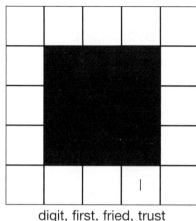

digit, first, fried, trust

39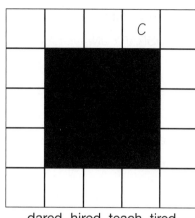

dared, hired, teach, tired

40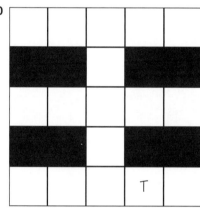

lifts, notes, quiet, thief

Choose two words, one from each set of brackets, to complete the sentences in the best way.

Example Tall is to (tree, <u>short</u>, colour) as narrow is to (thin, white, <u>wide</u>).

41 Tiny is to (large, minute, second) as broad is to (wide, fast, country).

42 Kind is to (unkind, generous, thoughtful) as slow is to (drive, quiet, quick).

43 Clean is to (cloth, spot, dirty) as bottom is to (top, lowest, chest).

44 Foot is to (hand, toe, knee) as hand is to (nail, leg, finger).

45 Cat is to (catfood, paws, whiskers) as fish is to (water, fins, net).

If the code for T E A C H is + − × ÷ @, what are the codes for the following words?

46 CAT _____   **47** HAT _____

What do these codes stand for?

48 + − × _____   **49** − × + _____   **50** ÷ @ − × + _____

5

B 15

5

B 24

5

Choose the word or phrase that makes each sentence true.

B 14

Example A LIBRARY always has (posters, a carpet, <u>books</u>, DVDs, stairs).

51 A SANDWICH always has (ham, lettuce, bread, tomato, butter).

52 A HORSE always has (hoofs, hay, a rider, a saddle, a stable).

53 A CAR always has (air conditioning, a radio, a CD player, four doors, wheels).

54 A BEACH always has (sand, umbrellas, chairs, plants, water).

55 A BOOK always has (drawings, pages, photographs, stories, poems).

5

Underline two words, one from each group, that go together to form a new word. The word in the first group always comes first.

B 8

Example (hand, <u>green</u>, for)   (light, <u>house</u>, sure)

56 (along, side, down)   (shot, stairs, wall)

57 (long, month, week)   (time, off, end)

58 (torch, gold, hot)   (burn, streak, light)

59 (must, left, pass)   (age, only, know)

60 (he, self, man)   (mind, or, and)

61 (girl, life, run)   (high, watch, guard)

62 (set, lift, kit)   (ten, hand, glow)

7

Rearrange the muddled letters in capitals to make a proper word. The answer will complete the sentence sensibly.

B 18

Example A BEZAR is an animal with stripes.   ZEBRA

63 Please don't walk on the AGRSS.   _____

64 My favourite flower is the SORE.   _____

65 Be careful when you cut with a EIKFN.   _____

3

Now go to the Progress Chart to record your score!   Total   65

Paper 4

Underline the two words, one from each group, which are closest in meaning.

B 3

Example (race, shop, <u>start</u>)   (finish, <u>begin</u>, end)

1 (health, remedy, doctor)   (chemist, right, cure)

2 (disturb, drill, hasty)   (slow, upset, rush)

3 (tell, offer, demand)   (insist, charge, buy)

4 (travel, area, map)   (direction, house, region)

5 (vast, heavy, size)   (huge, shape, inches)

5

Find the three-letter word which can be added to the letters in capitals to make a new word. The new word will complete the sentence sensibly.

B 22

Example The cat sprang onto the MO. <u>USE</u>

6 Callum is in HOSAL as he broke his arm. _____

7–8 Ethan enjoys eating lots of GES and OGES. _____ _____

9–10 Clare would RAT have some EAPPLE. _____ _____

5

Find the letter which will end the first word and start the second word.

B 10

Example peac (h) ome

11 luc (___) now   12 las (___) ive

13 lam (___) rince   14 han (___) ice

15 fin (___) ee

5

Here are five words. They can have a prefix of either SOME or BACK. Write S or B.

B 11

16 ___ ground   17 ___ body

18 ___ fire   19 ___ hand

20 ___ how

5

Write the four-letter word hidden at the end of one word and the beginning of the next word. The order of the letters may not be changed.

B 21

Example The children had bats and balls. <u>sand</u>

21 All airports must be warned. _____

22 I was sure he had one. _____

23 They are stored in the shed. _____

24 The rest of them went home. _____

25 If you don't want a pear change it for an apple. _____

5

Change the first word of the third pair in the same way as the other pairs to give a new word.

B 18

Example bind, hind   bare, hare   but, <u>hut</u>

26 pack, peck   ball, bell   band, _____

27 sing, wing   sink, wink   sail, _____

28 mile, lime   sent, nest   love, _____

29 peal, pale   bear, bare   deal, _____

30 hate, heat   fowl, flow   hire, _____

5

Complete the following sentences by selecting the most sensible word from each group of words given in the brackets. Underline the words selected.

Example The (<u>children</u>, books, foxes) carried the (houses, <u>books</u>, steps) home from the (greengrocer, <u>library</u>, factory).

31 The boy (grows, talks, likes) to eat (tomato sauce, ice cream, biscuits) with his (fork, plate, pasta).

32 The workman (knocked, pasted, glued) a large (hole, board, table) in the (wall, window, carpet) of his house.

33 The (river, road, moat) flowed (above, under, round) the (sky, bird, bridge).

34 John (tried, caught, dropped) to catch the (rope, ball, dog) before it (scored, lost, bounced).

35 The (giant, dwarf, queen) was so (clever, tall, ugly) he could touch the (ground, clouds, frog).

Find and underline the two words which need to change places for the sentence to make sense.

Example She went to <u>letter</u> the <u>write</u>.

36 Up try to clean it do.

37 Her writing a letter to I'm.

38 I like me book you gave the.

39 The better is weather now.

40 Acting you like do?

Find the missing number by using the two numbers outside the brackets in the same way as the other sets of numbers.

Example 2 [8] 4   3 [18] 6   5 [25] 5

41 18 [3] 6   20 [5] 4   16 [___] 8

42 2 [18] 9   3 [12] 4   6 [___] 4

43 11 [14] 3   5 [5] 0   8 [___] 7

44 10 [100] 10   4 [16] 4   8 [___] 8

45 13 [2] 11   10 [6] 4   9 [___] 8

Give the two missing groups of letters and numbers in the following sequences. The alphabet has been written out to help you.

A B C D E F G H I J K L M N O P Q R S T U V W X Y Z

Example CQ   DP   EQ   FP   GQ   HP

46 A2   C4   ___   ___   I10   K12

47 Az   ___   Cx   Dw   ___   Fu

48 GA   HB   ___   ___   KE   LF

49 Za   Yb   Xa   ___   ___   Ub

50 ___   E15   I12   M9   Q6   ___

Here are the number codes for four words. Match the right word to the right code.

RINK	KIN	INK	RANK
935	7159	7359	359

51 RINK _____   **52** RANK _____

53 INK _____   **54** KIN _____

55 Using the same code, which of these stands for NEAR?

3617   5717   5617   _____

Rearrange the letters of the word in capitals to make another word. The new word has something to do with the first two words.

Example   spot   soil   SAINT   STAIN

56 running   contest   CARE   _____

57 hazard   risk   GARDEN   _____

58 story   fable   LATE   _____

59 selfish   nasty   NAME   _____

60 weary   exhausted   TRIED   _____

If a = 10, b = 6, c = 3 and d = 2, find the answer to the following calculations.

61 $a - d =$ ___

62 $a \times c =$ ___

63 $a \div d =$ ___

64 $a + b + c =$ ___

65 $\dfrac{b}{c} =$ ___

Now go to the Progress Chart to record your score!   Total   65

Paper 5

1–5 Look at these groups.

M	G	C
Money	Gardening tools	Carpentry tools

Choose the correct group for each of the words below. Write the letter.

barrow ___   pound ___   dime ___   chisel ___

hammer ___   fork ___   spade ___   dollar ___

trowel ___   cent ___

Find the three-letter word which can be added to the letters in capitals to make a new word. The new word will complete the sentence sensibly.

B 22

Example The cat sprang onto the MO. <u>USE</u>

6 That's a big parcel. It says on it 'HLE with care'. _____

7 The DINGS on the walls were beautiful. _____

8 The trees in the FST were really huge. _____

9 She PRISED piano every day. _____

10 I am SED of monsters. _____

5

Find the letter which will end the first word and start the second word.

B 10

Example peac (h) ome

11 pian (___) pen   12 mean (___) here

13 heal (___) eat   14 fas (___) ick   15 spor (___) idy

5

If these words were written backwards and then placed in alphabetical order, which word would come fifth? Underline your answer.

B 20

16	slowly	happily	softly	friendly	normally
17	glanced	misplaced	polished	showed	charged
18	blacksmith	fifth	health	truth	warmth
19	vitamin	javelin	entertain	satin	captain
20	parent	absent	accident	confront	vacant

5

Write the four-letter word hidden at the end of one word and the beginning of the next word. The order of the letters may not be changed.

B 21

Example The children had bats and balls. <u>sand</u>

21 I heard a crash in your bedroom. _____

22 I started it at once. _____

23 My son likes to write stories. _____

24 When one dog barks the others all join in. _____

25 We started to dance as soon as music played. _____

5

Add one letter to the word in capital letters to make a new word. The meaning of the new word is given in the clue.

B 12

Example PLAN   simple   <u>plain</u>

26 TOOL   three-legged seat   _____

27 FIEND   a person one likes   _____

28 CLAP   to hold together firmly   _____

29 CAST   along the seashore   _____

30 SAY   to remain   _____

5

16

Complete the following sentences by selecting the most sensible word from each group of words given in the brackets. Underline the words selected.

B 14

Example The (children, books, foxes) carried the (houses, books, steps) home from the (greengrocer, library, factory).

31 The old man likes to eat (potatoes, rice pudding, bananas) before he goes to (work, garden, sleep) but he can't find a place to leave the (cores, peel, skins) near his bed.

32 This (afternoon, yesterday, house) we are going on a school (desk, visit, yard) to the town (museum, railings, sky).

33 Can't you be (good, quick, quiet)? You're too (big, clumsy, noisy). I'm trying to (cook, play, work).

34 When on holiday I like to (visit, buy, sell) souvenirs so that I when I get (home, away, tired) I (forget, remember, enjoy) what a good time I had.

35 The (fire brigade, police, vet) came quickly to the (farm, animals, blaze) with their (dogs, hats, hoses).

5

Choose two words, one from each set of brackets, to complete the sentence in the best way.

B 15

Example Tall is to (tree, short, colour) as narrow is to (thin, white, wide).

36 Same is to (similar, opposite, change) as day is to (long, night, sleep).

37 Add is to (number, subtract, plus) as divide is to (minus, multiply, figures).

38 Expand is to (lessen, shrink, widen) as reduce is to (cover, unfold, shorten).

39 Unite is to (slit, repair, join) as new is to (modern, old, out of date).

40 Finish is to (rest, end, lose) as magnificent is to (damaged, grand, terrible).

5

Underline the two words, one from each group, which are closest in meaning.

B 5

Example (race, shop, start)   (finish, begin, end)

41 (hotel, prison, house)   (office, jail, roof)

42 (difficult, short, slow)   (long, hard, never)

43 (present, empty, maybe)   (here, full, absent)

44 (big, heavy, remote)   (tiny, flat, distant)

45 (halt, recent, permanent)   (distant, temporary, stop)

5

If the code for S T E A M is a b c d e, what are the codes for the following words?

B 24

46 M A S T _____   47 T A M E _____

What do these codes stand for?

48 e c a a _____   49 e d b c _____   50 a c d b _____

5

17

If a = 2, b = 3, d = 4, e = 5, f = 6, g = 8, find the value of these words.

Give your answers as letters.

51 g − b = ___   **52** f ÷ a = ___   **53** (e + d) − f = ___

54 2a = ___   **55** a + b = ___

B 26
5

Underline the one word in the brackets which will go equally well with both the pairs of words outside the brackets.

B 3

Example   rush, attack   cost, fee   (price, hasten, strike, <u>charge</u>, money)

56 apartment, rooms   level, even   (flat, home, smooth, habitat, ledge)

57 clue, lead   central, important   (hint, lock, key, trail, essential)

58 apple, grape   red, yellow   (pear, pineapple, brown, rose, orange)

59 price, debt   beak, snout   (invoice, leaflet, nose, paw, bill)

60 stone, boulder   sway, move   (cliff, hill, swing, step, rock)

5

Change one word so that the sentence makes sense. Underline the word you are taking out and write your new word on the line.

B 14

Example   I waited in line to buy a <u>book</u> to see the film.   *ticket*

61 She put the milk in the oven to keep it cool.   _____

62 My dog laughs when people ring the doorbell.   _____

63 I put a coin on the envelope before I posted it.   _____

64 The bicycle's saddles went round and round.   _____

65 November is the last week of the year.   _____

5

Now go to the Progress Chart to record your score!   Total   65

Paper 6

Underline the two words which are the odd ones out in the following groups of words.

B 4

Example   black   <u>king</u>   purple   green   <u>house</u>

1 house   road   bungalow   castle   path

2 swim   coat   sweater   dive   t-shirt

3 kneel   sit   walk   hop   skip

4 butter   cake   bread   bun   flour

5 onion   apple   plum   cabbage   potato

5

Find the three-letter word which can be added to the letters in capitals to make a new word. The new word will complete the sentence sensibly.

B 22

Example The cat sprang onto the MO. <u>USE</u>

6 I cycled along a NAR lane. _____

7 I'm thirsty, time to stop for a DR. _____

8 She wouldn't listen. I T her she'd have to do it. _____

9 We saw a polar B at the zoo. _____

10 H grows on our heads. _____

⑤

Find the letter which will end the first word and start the second word.

B 10

Example peac (<u>h</u>) ome

11 spen (___) anger

12 mos (___) ribe

13 lea (___) lood

14 stra (___) ood

15 firs (___) ender

⑤

Underline the one word which **cannot be made** from the letters of the word in capital letters.

B 7

Example STATIONERY stone tyres ration <u>nation</u> noisy

16 TERRACE	car	rate	trace	erase	crate
17 DISTANT	stead	stand	stain	ants	dint
18 PAINTER	trip	rain	tramp	nape	print
19 GENERAL	large	near	rage	gear	ages
20 DETAINS	staid	instead	near	neat	site

⑤

Write the four-letter word hidden at the end of one word and the beginning of the next word. The order of the letters may not be changed.

B 21

Example The children had bats and balls. <u>sand</u>

21 Harry's top was covered in mud. _____

22 We are not going there. _____

23 The shops will be open so we will go tomorrow. _____

24 Stars and angels gave the sign. _____

25 As it is raining shall we eat lunch inside? _____

⑤

Change the first word of the third pair in the same way as the other pairs to give a new word.

B 18

Example bind, hind bare, hare but, <u>hut</u>

26 tint, stint trap, strap tale, _____

19

27 gate, grate	pick, prick	tick, _____
28 same, lame	sate, late	sack, _____
29 same, mate	bare, rate	page, _____
30 grip, rip	blot, lot	ship, _____

5

Find and underline the two words which need to change places for the sentence to make sense.

B 17

Example She went to <u>letter</u> the <u>write</u>.

31 I am this up with fed food.

32 Were chess playing they?

33 Did win team the or lose?

34 Let's my to go house.

35 Where it I put shall?

5

Choose two words, one from each set of brackets, to complete the sentence in the best way.

B 15

Example Smile is to happiness as (drink, <u>tear</u>, shout) is to (whisper, laugh, <u>sorrow</u>).

36 Today is to yesterday as (May, June, July) is to (August, May, March).

37 Two is to hands as (4, 5, 10) is to (toes, ears, thumbs).

38 Roof is to house as (window, wall, ceiling) is to (cover, room, floor).

39 Black is to white as (snow, rain, cold) is to (hot, sun, warm).

40 Cat is to animal as (dog, robin, cow) is to (air, bird, fish).

5

Fill in the crosswords so that all the given words are included. You have been given one letter as a clue in each crossword.

B 19

41

cared, comic, court, timid

42

early, Egypt, evade, yacht

43

clear, madam, major, music

44

prove, pushy, treat, store

45

meals, motor, repay, plant

5

If the letters in the following words were arranged in alphabetical order, which letter would come in the middle?

B 20

46 gruel _____

47 exhaust _____

If these words were listed in reverse alphabetical order, which word would come second?

48 charade	chorus	chamber	chemist	chivalry
49 fraction	friction	frostbite	frown	friend
50 trampoline	train	trophy	treasure	trellis

5

If a = 1, b = 2, c = 3, d = 4, e = 5, f = 6, find the value of the following calculations.

B 26

51 abc = ___

52 cde = ___

53 bcd = ___

54 ef = ___

55 cf + be = ___

5

Solve the problems by working out the letter codes. The alphabet has been written out to help you.

B 24

A B C D E F G H I J K L M N O P Q R S T U V W X Y Z

Example   In a code, SECOND is written as UGEQPF. How would you write THIRD?
VJKTF

56 In a code, ARRIVE is written as ZQQHUD. How would you write REAR? _____

57 In a code, LISTEN is written as MJTUFO. How would you write NEST? _____

58 In a code, PLANE is written as RNCPG. What does NCR mean?   _____

59 In a code, BEAR is written as ADZQ. How would you write KING?   _____

60 In a code, VOWEL is written as UNVDK. What does EHMC mean?   _____

5

Which one letter can be added to the front of all of these words to make new words?

B 12

Example   _c_are   _c_at   _c_rate   _c_all

61 ___eat   ___one   ___ice   ___ote

62 ___ail   ___ape   ___ear   ___here

63 ___act   ___lag   ___all   ___ace

64 ___ill   ___end   ___lack   ___last

65 ___air   ___all   ___and   ___old

5

Now go to the Progress Chart to record your score!   Total   **65**

Paper 7

Underline the word in the brackets closest in meaning to the word in capitals.

B 5

Example   UNHAPPY   (unkind   death   laughter   <u>sad</u>   friendly)

1 EDGE   (centre   outside   rim   bottom   top)

2 DOZE   (blanket   start   nap   bed   awake)

3 LITTER   (bins   sweep   brush   rubbish   paper)

4 DIFFICULT   (easy   understand   answer   soft   hard)

5 TALE   (book   story   read   paper   library)

5

Underline the pair of words most opposite in meaning.

B 9

Example   cup, mug   coffee, milk   <u>hot, cold</u>

6 tall, high   wide, narrow   long, thin

7 hot, warm   clean, tidy   near, far

8 deep, shallow	rush, hurry	occupy, fill
9 open, shut	pause, stop	provide, supply
10 leave, exit	borrow, lend	damp, moist

5

Find the letter which will end the first word and start the second word.

B 10

Example   peac (h) ome

11 gon (___) low   12 hav (___) ver   13 pas (___) ave

14 man (___) ard   15 los (___) ray

5

Find a word that can be put in front of each of the following words to make new, compound words.

B 11

Example	cast	fall	ward	pour	_down_
16 show	board	light	step		_____
17 look	line	back	board		_____
18 sleep	take	rule	priced		_____
19 noon	care	taste	thought		_____
20 bike	car	way	boat		_____

5

Write the four-letter word hidden at the end of one word and the beginning of the next word. The order of the letters may not be changed.

B 21

Example   The children had bats and balls.   _sand_

21 Some of his ideas were quite wrong.   _____

22 My temperature was back to normal this morning.   _____

23 First of all we will wash up.   _____

24 I wish other people would pick up their rubbish.   _____

25 There was a large wasp in the jam.   _____

5

Change the first word into the last word by changing one letter at a time and making a new, different word in the middle.

B 13

Example   CASE _CASH_ LASH

26 FISH   _____   FAST

27 LOAN   _____   TOAD

28 CODE   _____   HOPE

29 FILL   _____   MILK

30 WILD   _____   SILT

5

Complete the following sentences by selecting the most sensible word from each group of words given in the brackets. Underline the words selected.

B 14

Example The (<u>children</u>, books, foxes) carried the (houses, <u>books</u>, steps) home from the (greengrocer, <u>library</u>, factory).

31 Every (day, morning, birthday) my (dog, cat, mother) makes me a special (loaf, cake, bun).

32 The woman (sighed, screamed, sang) as she was so (hot, cold, frightened) by the scary (rug, film, mug)

33 The secret (door, stairway, message) had been written on the (hand, cupboard, parchment) by the (mother, mouse, pirate).

34 He (wrote, thought, ran) as quickly as possible to the (cows, stones, police) to raise the (price, roof, alarm).

35 'Put your (feet, sticks, hands) up if you know the (question, time, answer),' said the (king, friend, teacher).

5

Find and underline the two words which need to change places for each sentence to make sense.

B 17

Example She went to <u>letter</u> the <u>write</u>.

36 My beautifully is work neat.

37 The badly is carpet stained.

38 Can you down the volume turn?

39 Some was given I flowers.

40 Don't to try move please.

5

Solve the problems by working out the letter codes. The alphabet has been written out to help you.

B 24

A B C D E F G H I J K L M N O P Q R S T U V W X Y Z

Example In a code, SECOND is written as UGEQPF. How would you write THIRD?
VJKTF

41 In a code, CHILDREN is written as DIJMESFO. How would you write RIDE? _____

42 In a code, PLEASE is written as RNGCUG. How would you write LEAP? _____

43 In a code, STEP is written as TUFQ. How would you write COAL? _____

44 In a code, DUST is written as BSQR. What does BMMP mean? _____

45 In a code, MILK is written as OKNM. What does VKR mean? _____

5

Fill in the crosswords so that all the given words are included. You have been given one letter as a clue in each crossword.

46

house, laser, litre, upset

47

greed, lapse, paste, steep

48

fudge, march, order, stone

49

allow, expel, super, trees

50

bread, catch, enter, farms

If these words were listed in reverse alphabetical order, which word would come second?

| **51** | clasp | clamp | close | cloak | clock | _____ |
| **52** | empty | glass | fruit | glove | elect | _____ |

If these words were placed in alphabetical order, which word would come fourth?

53 human   hound   honey   house   hours   _____

54 region   parade   patrol   reason   reader   _____

4

If e = 1, f = 2, d = 3, c = 4, b = 6, a = 9, find the answer to the following calculations.

B 26

55 $c - d =$ ___   **56** $b + e =$ ___   **57** $2a - e =$ ___

58 $\dfrac{b}{f} =$ ___   **59** $ad =$ ___   **60** $bc - a =$ ___

6

Which of the following form words when spelt backwards? Underline them.

B 20

61 MUST   MOOR   MALE   MIST   MARK

62 WINK   WENT   WANT   WAKE   WOLF

63 TRAP   MEWS   MILL   MONK   MAST

64 PADS   PENS   PEAS   SEED   SWAP

65 EMIT   TUNE   AMID   EXIT   TINT

5

Now go to the Progress Chart to record your score!   Total 65

Paper 8

Look at these three groups.

B 1

	A	B	C
	Flowers	Fruit	Trees

1–5 Choose the correct group for each of the words below. Write in the letter.

grape ___   ash ___   bluebell ___   elm ___

lily ___   melon ___   willow ___   kiwi ___

oak ___   crocus ___

5

Underline the pair of words most opposite in meaning.

B 9

    Example cup, mug coffee, milk <u>hot, cold</u>

6 east, west   disease, sickness   upset, worry

7 sand, beach   black, white   street, road

8 choose, select   omen, sign   divide, multiply

9 whole, total   cheap, expensive   force, compel

10 level, even   last, end   fail, succeed

5

Find the letter which will end the first word and start the second word.

B 10

Example   peac (h) ome

11 car (___) win   **12** cal (___) ose   **13** mes (___) hut

14 bea (___) rum   **15** sho (___) ind

5

Underline two words, one from each group, that go together to form a new word. The word in the first group always comes first.

B 8

Example   (hand, green, for)   (light, house, sure)

16 (foot, grown, dear)   (move, come, print)

17 (whole, quarter, half)   (path, way, tumble)

18 (in, out, but)   (break, crash, tumble)

19 (ear, eye, lid)   (sign, scar, ache)

20 (wide, lag, broad)   (chair, cast, road)

5

Write the four-letter word hidden at the end of one word and the beginning of the next word. The order of the letters may not be changed.

B 21

Example   The children had bats and balls.   sand

21 Ice helps lower the temperature of your drink.   _____

22 Quickly come to the window and see the fireworks!   _____

23 My homework is as easy to do as ever.   _____

24 He asked me to move nearer.   _____

25 Because the bus was so late, you're in a rush.   _____

5

Change the first word into the last word by changing one letter at a time and making a new, different word in the middle.

B 13

Example   CASE CASH LASH

26 RAIN   _____   HAIL   **27** SOME   _____   COMB

28 THIN   _____   THAT   **29** WILL   _____   FULL

30 PINE   _____   FIND

5

Fill in the missing letters and numbers. The alphabet has been written out to help you.

B 23

A B C D E F G H I J K L M N O P Q R S T U V W X Y Z

Example   AB is to CD as PQ is to RS.

31 AC is to BD as JL is to _____.

32 ACE is to CEG as LNP is to _____.

33 EH is to IL as MP is to _____.

34 5QR is to 6ST as 7UV is to _____.

35 3CE is to 5DF as 7EG is to _____.

5

Fill in the crosswords so that all the given words are included. You have been given one letter as a clue in each crossword.

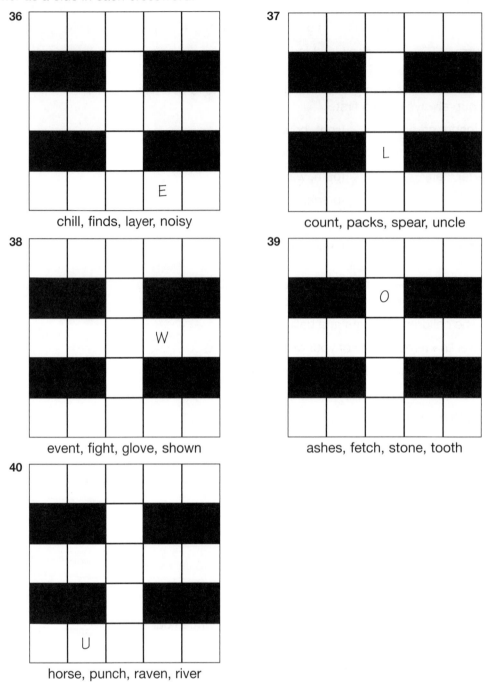

36 chill, finds, layer, noisy

37 count, packs, spear, uncle

38 event, fight, glove, shown

39 ashes, fetch, stone, tooth

40 horse, punch, raven, river

5

Underline the one word in brackets which will go equally well with both the pairs of words outside the brackets.

Example rush, attack   cost, fee   (price, hasten, strike, <u>charge</u>, money)

41 protect, shield   pillow, pad   (sofa, bedding, cushion, bandage)

42 smoulder, blaze   shoot, detonate   (trigger, excite, fire, launch)

Paper 1

1 easy, simple
2 go, depart
3 new, fresh
4 tired, weary
5 hide, conceal
6 sell, purchase
7 dim, bright
8 back, front
9 question, answer
10 accept, refuse
11 farmer, shed, milk the cows
12 spade, beach, castle
13 forget, post, letter
14 eagle, food, nest
15 lantern, face, buried
16 PLATE, PETAL
17 SHORE, HORSE
18 TABLE, BLEAT
19 HEADS, SHADE
20 LEAST, STALE
21 ever
22 hero
23 rear
24 soft
25 ends
26 e
27 k
28 t
29 l
30 t
31 today, feel
32 tights, it
33 hairdo, your
34 glass, I've
35 home, have
36 GH
37 JL
38 P8
39 18BC
40 2DE
41 f
42 s
43 w
44 p
45 d

46–50

51 * : ! ?
52 £ : ! *
53 / ! : £
54 TRAP
55 REAL
56 beak
57 roots
58 sole
59 walls
60 sleeves
61 tree
62 lean
63 sand
64 fame
65 spin

Paper 2

1 alter, change
2 fear, fright
3 fidget, wriggle
4 hard, difficult
5 start, begin
6 shiny, dull
7 generous, mean
8 home, away
9 often, seldom
10 raise, lower
11 nameless
12 keepsake
13 behead
14 textbook
15 keyboard
16 TEA
17 ROW
18 EAT
19 ARM
20 ASK

21 scan
22 heal
23 herb
24 item
25 them
26 SAND
27 MAKE
28 DEAL
29 BALL
30 COME
31 sheep, field, grass
32 tiger, cage, zoo
33 stone, frog, flies
34 old, up, steep
35 move, snake, rock
36 April, May
37 lamb, sheep
38 artist, picture
39 cup, drink
40 uncle, nephew

41–45

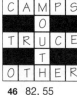

46 82, 55
47 $\frac{1}{2}$, 1
48 63, 56
49 99, 110
50 7, 8
51 ○△🍎🍎
52 △🍎🍎◆
53 ○■🍎🍎
54 △🍎🍎
55 ○■🍎🍎◆
56 b
57 l
58 e
59 t
60 g
61 ACHE
62 BEGIN
63 BELOW
64 CHEAP
65 MALE

Bond Verbal Reasoning Assessment Papers 9–10 years Book 1

Paper 3

1 hail
2 stable
3 carrots
4 speak
5 toddlers
6 spend, save
7 same, different
8 quit, start
9 crowded, deserted
10 hurt, heal
11 e
12 t
13 d
14 r
15 l
16 foot
17 up
18 book
19 in
20 head
21 tool
22 mesh
23 them
24 head
25 heap
26 broken, chair
27 enough, you
28 untidy, my
29 now, do
30 cup, I'll
31 51 83
32 85 65
33 108 60
34 34 26
35 27 32

36–40

41 minute, wide
42 unkind, quick
43 dirty, top
44 toe, finger

45 paws, fins
46 ÷ × +
47 @ × +
48 TEA
49 EAT
50 CHEAT
51 bread
52 hoofs
53 wheels
54 water
55 pages
56 downstairs
57 weekend
58 torchlight
59 passage
60 manor
61 lifeguard
62 kitten
63 GRASS
64 ROSE
65 KNIFE

Paper 4

1 remedy, cure
2 disturb, upset
3 demand, insist
4 area, region
5 vast, huge
6 PIT
7 RAP
8 RAN
9 HER
10 PIN
11 k
12 h
13 p
14 d
15 s
16 B
17 S
18 B
19 B
20 S
21 lair
22 done
23 rest
24 here
25 arch
26 bend
27 wail
28 vole
29 dale
30 heir
31 likes, tomato sauce, pasta
32 knocked, hole, wall
33 river, under, bridge
34 tried, ball, bounced
35 giant, tall, clouds
36 up, do
37 her, I'm
38 me, the

39 better, weather
40 acting, do
41 2
42 24
43 15
44 64
45 1
46 E6   G8
47 By   Ev
48 IC   JD
49 Wb   Va
50 A18   U3
51 7359
52 7159
53 359
54 935
55 5617
56 RACE
57 DANGER
58 TALE
59 MEAN
60 TIRED
61 8
62 30
63 5
64 19
65 2

Paper 5

1–5 *Give one mark for each two correct answers:* barrow G, pound M, dime M, chisel C, hammer C, fork G, spade G, dollar M, trowel G, cent M
6 AND
7 RAW
8 ORE
9 ACT
10 CAR
11 o
12 t
13 s
14 t
15 t
16 slowly
17 showed
18 truth
19 satin
20 confront
21 shin
22 edit
23 test
24 none
25 west
26 stool
27 friend
28 clamp or clasp
29 coast
30 stay
31 bananas, sleep, skins
32 afternoon, visit, museum

Bond Verbal Reasoning Assessment Papers 9–10 years Book 1

33 quiet, noisy, work
34 buy, home, remember
35 fire brigade, blaze, hoses
36 opposite, night
37 subtract, multiply
38 widen, shorten
39 join, modern
40 end, grand
41 prison, jail
42 difficult, hard
43 present, here
44 remote, distant
45 halt, stop
46 edab
47 bdec
48 MESS
49 MATE
50 SEAT
51 e
52 b
53 b
54 d
55 e
56 flat
57 key
58 orange
59 bill
60 rock
61 oven, fridge
62 laughs, barks
63 coin, stamp
64 saddles, wheels
65 week, month

Paper 6

1 road, path
2 swim, dive
3 kneel, sit
4 butter, flour
5 apple, plum
6 ROW
7 INK
8 OLD
9 EAR
10 AIR
11 d
12 t
13 f
14 w
15 t
16 erase
17 stead
18 tramp
19 ages
20 near
21 stop
22 wear
23 pens
24 sand
25 chin
26 stale

27 trick
28 lack
29 gate
30 hip
31 this, fed
32 chess, they
33 win, the
34 my, go
35 it, shall
36 June, May
37 10, toes
38 ceiling, room
39 cold, hot
40 robin, bird

41–45

46 l
47 s
48 chivalry
49 frostbite
50 trellis
51 6
52 60
53 24
54 30
55 28
56 QDZQ
57 OFTU
58 LAP
59 JHMF
60 FIND
61 n
62 t
63 f
64 b
65 h

Paper 7

1 rim
2 nap
3 rubbish
4 hard

5 story
6 wide, narrow
7 near, far
8 deep, shallow
9 open, shut
10 borrow, lend
11 g
12 e
13 s
14 y
15 t
16 side
17 out
18 over
19 after
20 motor
21 side
22 malt
23 fall
24 shot
25 spin
26 FIST
27 LOAD
28 COPE
29 MILL
30 WILT
31 birthday, mother, cake
32 screamed, frightened, film
33 message, parchment, pirate
34 ran, police, alarm
35 hands, answer, teacher
36 beautifully, work
37 badly, carpet
38 volume, the
39 some, I
40 to, try
41 SJEF
42 NGCR
43 DPBM
44 DOOR
45 TIP

46–50

Bond Verbal Reasoning Assessment Papers 9–10 years Book 1

51 clock
52 glass
53 house
54 reason
55 1
56 7
57 17
58 3
59 27
60 15
61 MOOR
62 WOLF
63 TRAP
64 SWAP
65 EMIT

Paper 8

1–5 *Give one mark for each two correct answers:* grape B, ash C, bluebell A, elm C, lily A, melon B, willow C, kiwi B, oak C, crocus A
6 east, west
7 black, white
8 divide, multiply
9 cheap, expensive
10 fail, succeed
11 t
12 l
13 s
14 d
15 w
16 footprint
17 halfway
18 outbreak
19 earache
20 broadcast
21 slow
22 wand
23 seas
24 oven
25 rein
26 RAIL
27 COME
28 THAN
29 FILL
30 FINE
31 KM
32 NPR
33 QT
34 8WX
35 9FH

36–40

F	I	N	D	S		C	O	U	N	T
		O					N			
C	H	I	L	L		P	A	C	K	S
		S					L			
L	A	Y	E	R		S	P	E	A	R

F	I	G	H	T		F	E	T	C	H
		L					O			
S	H	O	W	N		S	T	O	N	E
		V					T			
E	V	E	N	T		A	S	H	E	S

H	O	R	S	E
		A		
R	I	V	E	R
		E		
P	U	N	C	H

41 cushion
42 fire
43 bright
44 net
45 spring
46 TIN
47 ORE
48 TWO
49 LOT
50 SAT
51 48
52 95
53 88
54 84
55 10
56 15
57 10
58 12
59 48
60 1
61 EINOQSTU
62 N
63 S
64 EIMPR
65 M

Paper 9

1 power
2 coast
3 herd
4 collar
5 clock
6 BUTTER
7 GRUBBY
8 ELEPHANT
9 LITTER
10 ENVELOPES
11 AND
12 RIP

13 FUN
14 ARK
15 EAR
16 bat
17 cost
18 ever
19 pane
20 sing
21 oval
22 were
23 rope
24 itch
25 tone
26 ear, blink
27 pan, flit
28 and, flake
29 one, dwell
30 sun, petal
31 shirt, football, team
32 sharpener, bag, chair
33 ship, harbour, slowly
34 listened, hear, coming
35 Antarctic, huge, houses
36 29
37 14
38 1
39 24
40 72

41–45

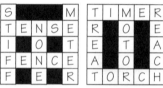

S			M		T	I	M	E	R
T	E	N	S	E	R		O		E
I		O		T	E		T		A
F	E	N	C	E	A		O		C
F			R		T	O	R	C	H

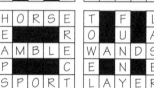

H	O	R	S	E		T		F		L
E			R		O		U		A
A	M	B	L	E	W	A	N	D	S
P			C		E		N		E
S	P	O	R	T		L	A	Y	E	R

H	O	V	E	R
		I		U
S	T	E	A	M
		W		M
N	A	S	T	Y

46 STONE
47 DARE
48 SHRUB
49 CRATE
50 REAR
51 PIE
52 KIN
53 ARE
54 PAW
55 ACT
56 lonely

57 march
58 rascal
59 square
60 puppets
61–65 2 = Whites, 3 = Blues,
4 = Greys, 5 = Greens,
6 = Blacks

Paper 10

1 bend, curve
2 small, slight
3 ruin, destroy
4 author, writer
5 fast, swift
6 BAG
7 ONE
8 APE
9 MAT
10 OAT
11 have
12 throb
13 core
14 rope
15 sand
16 hiss
17 mash
18 stir
19 meat
20 romp
21 far, cane
22 soil, peat
23 host, paint
24 hunt, laid
25 dear, sport
26 school, important, wonders
27 found, umbrella, rain
28 fire, building, quickly
29 cat, black, collar
30 drank, put on, left
31 better, weather
32 supper, looking
33 me, the
34 up, do
35 vase, knocked
36 D79
37 G20
38 F18
39 GH8
40 QRS
41 still, active
42 warm, cool
43 bend, straighten
44 fix, destroy
45 low, high
46 garland
47 gallop
48 g, a
49 gallop

50 6
51 l h j b
52 g h l b
53 DEAN
54 STAIN
55 guests
56 coat
57 food
58 a steering wheel
59 rules
60 add, reduce
61 lose, tie
62 catch, free
63 give, accept
64 command, request
65 delete, circle

Paper 11

1 shout, yell
2 need, require
3 bench, chair
4 ask, enquire
5 close, shut
6 PEN
7 ASH
8 ARC
9 WAR
10 LIP
11 n
12 i
13 h
14 t
15 o
16 snow
17 hand
18 water
19 under
20 some
21 heap
22 iris
23 sold
24 none
25 wear
26 SLAY
27 CHAT
28 PAST
29 DIRE
30 LUCK
31 new, which
32 wet, towel
33 borrow, you
34 very, said
35 cover, like
36 numbers, letters
37 light, dark
38 run, fly
39 string, rope
40 flowers, vegetables

41–45

```
U N F I T   P   F   S
N   I       A L L O W
T R E A T   R   A   E
I   L       K   K   L
L A D E N   S P E L L

L A D L E   R O B E S
  R   V       E   P
T R I B E   C R A T E
  V   N       C   A
G R E A T   O T H E R

U   S   C
S U P E R
U   O   E
A N K L E
L   E   K
```

46 CN DO
47 5R 17Z
48 ZA WD
49 YR AN
50 GFE HGF
51 TEAR
52 PEST
53 MEAL
54 HOSE
55 BEARD
56 24
57 60
58 JMU
59 NUT
60 FUN
61 MDWS
62 IPMJEBZ
63 band
64 rough
65 sweet

Paper 12

1 lead, iron
2 mountain, hill
3 cross, angry
4 sun, moon
5 rest, sleep
6 NOW
7 VAN
8 EAR
9 RIM
10 RAT
11 bluebell
12 sunshine
13 footstep
14 afterwards
15 football
16 pour
17 calf
18 chap
19 lint

20 etch
21 team, keys
22 flat, hero
23 tall, skin
24 bead, fore
25 pint, rate
26 tried, son, homework
27 sign, road, stop
28 plane, sky, flying
29 walked, fast, castle
30 highwaymen, coach, gold
31 NP
32 YZ
33 MOQ
34 DW
35 FGE

36–40

41 fruit, meat
42 draw, wear
43 read, eat
44 stars, crosses
45 hot, windy
46 5761
47 27651
48 562
49 5762
50 8651
51 evening, morning
52 ordinary, unusual
53 swift, steady
54 tilted, straight
55 ride, walk
56 9
57 3
58 y
59 p
60 n
61 s
62 d
63 trout
64 home
65 mist

Paper 13

1–5 *Give one mark for each two correct answers:* bridge B, drill C, ferret A, baboon A, arcade B, rose D, cinema B, beige D, mole A, saw C
6 break, mend
7 stretch, shrink
8 empty, full
9 plentiful, scarce
10 winner, loser
11 b
12 e
13 s
14 y
15 t
16 stain
17 stead
18 tramp
19 ages
20 clean
21 alto
22 idea
23 hare
24 seas
25 tour
26 HEAR
27 FARM
28 BULK
29 WINE
30 SENT
31 sunny, woman, beach
32 spring, green, lambs
33 quickly, station, train
34 boat, rock, water
35 jumped, cold, swam
36 lie
37 pack
38 star
39 kind
40 cold

41–45

46 DP FU
47 8R 4T
48 CB FC
49 8A 5Z
50 FU EV
51 ○ ◆ 💬 ①
52 ① ◆ ○
53 TAG
54 TEA
55 GREAT
56 8945
57 31754
58 FACED
59 HEDGED
60 BEACH
61 act
62 belt
63 know
64 moor
65 sty

Paper 14

1 appreciation, thanks
2 creak, squeak
3 gallant, brave
4 rubbish, litter
5 silence, quietness
6 n
7 r
8 d
9 m
10 d
11 even
12 deep
13 part
14 joyful
15 end
16 TRAP
17 TEAM
18 DRAG
19 STEM
20 PORT
21 nothing
22 carpet
23 landmark
24 another
25 bedstead
26 leap
27 skin
28 tall
29 farm
30 tool
31 BAKE
32 MARK
33 MAKE
34 LONG
35 COLT
36 borrow, you
37 shoes, are
38 one, buy
39 it, I'll

40 full, hope
41 finish, conclude
42 freeze, cool
43 second, minute
44 ebb, flow
45 noon, day
46 money
47 a lens
48 keys
49 a seat
50 child
51 ❞○○①
52 ①○◆①
53 GEAR
54 EAGER
55 GAVE
56 20
57 15
58 12
59 15
60 16
61 R
62 G
63 D
64 S
65 M

Paper 15

1 <u>summer</u>, winter
2 <u>newspapers</u>, invitations
3 <u>sings</u>, reads
4 <u>monkey</u>, lion
5 <u>flower</u>, tree
6 front, back
7 rough, smooth
8 bent, straight
9 sell, buy
10 here, there
11 hose
12 raps
13 warm
14 this
15 seat
16 rain
17 fire
18 tooth
19 road
20 moon
21 news
22 then
23 hear
24 duet
25 fund
26 FREE

27 DEAD
28 ISLE
29 BRAT
30 BARK
31 street, you
32 wilting, hot
33 paper, used
34 blissfully, cat
35 in, sick
36 answer
37 find
38 study
39 believe
40 lengthy

41–45

46 REASON
47 SCARED
48 DELIVER
49 CHASE
50 BOAST
51 1 ◆ 3 0 7
52 1 ◆ 4 3 △
53 △ 4 3 0
54 △ 3 0 7
55 0 4 3 1 ◆
56 k
57 b
58 e
59 n
60 l
61 bare
62 main
63 raft
64 cover
65 short

43 light, dazzling   clever, intelligent   (scholar, sunshine, clear, bright)

44 web, snare   catch, trawl   (fish, net, spider, fishermen)

45 summer, winter   jump, leap   (autumn, season, spring, hop)

5

46 If 8124 stands for PINT, 412 stands for _____.

B 24

47 If 9463 stands for ROSE, 493 stands for _____.

48 If 7542 stands for TOWN, 745 stands for _____.

49 If 9744 stands for TOLL, 479 stands for _____.

50 If 4578 stands for FAST, 758 stands for _____.

5

51–54 Five children did a test for which 100 marks were awarded.

B 25

    R got 96 marks.

    M had half as many marks as the person who was first.

    G lost 5 marks.

    D had 7 fewer than G.

    S has 12 marks fewer than R.

How many marks did these children get?

    M ___   G ___   D___   S ___

4

If $a = 2$, $b = 3$, $c = 4$ and $d = 8$, find the answer to the following calculations.

B 26

55 $(d - a) + c =$ _____

56 $(a + b) \times b =$ _____

57 $a + a + b + b =$ _____

58 $(d \div c) \times 2b =$ _____

59 $2a \times b \times c =$ _____

60 $d - b - c =$ _____

6

Answer these questions. The alphabet has been written out to help you.

B 20

    A B C D E F G H I J K L M N O P Q R S T U V W X Y Z

61 Put the letters in the word QUESTION in alphabetical order.   _____

62 Which is now the 3rd letter?   ____

63 Which is now the 6th letter?   ____

64 Put the letters in the word PRIME in alphabetical order.   _____

65 Which is now the middle letter?   ____

5

Paper 9

Find a word that is similar in meaning to the word in capital letters and that rhymes with the second word.

Example   CABLE   tyre   _wire_

1 ELECTRICITY   tower   _____

2 SHORELINE   toast   _____

3 A LOT OF CATTLE   word   _____

4 PART OF A SHIRT   dollar   _____

5 TIMEPIECE   mock   _____

Rearrange the muddled letters in capitals to make a proper word. The answer will complete the sentence sensibly.

Example   A BEZAR is an animal with stripes.   _ZEBRA_

6 We spread TTREBU on bread.   _____

7 Children often have BYRUGB knees!   _____

8 The African LPHEEANT has big ears.   _____

9 Put your TRELTI in the bin!   _____

10 We put letters in NVEEESLOP.   _____

Find the three-letter word which can be added to the letters in capitals to make a new word. The new word will complete the sentence sensibly.

Example   The cat sprang onto the MO.   _USE_

11 Please wash your HS before lunch.   _____

12 The DPING tap kept me awake.   _____

13 She is very NY and makes us laugh a lot.   _____

14 It was much DER now that the lights had been turned off. _____

15 His HING was poor, he couldn't hear people talking.   _____

Remove one letter from the word in capital letters to leave a new word. The meaning of the new word is given in the clue.

Example   AUNT   an insect   _ant_

16 BEAT   a flying mammal   _____

17 COAST   the price of something   _____

18 FEVER   always   _____

19 PLANE   window glass   _____

20 SLING   a musical sound made by a voice   _____

Write the four-letter word hidden at the end of one word and the beginning of the next word. The order of the letters may not be changed.

B 21

Example   The children had bats and balls.   <u>sand</u>

21 Not only is the stamp attractive but it is also valuable.   _____

22 It was the tallest tower ever seen.   _____

23 My poor mother had four operations.   _____

24 Izzy's rabbit chewed a hole in her hutch.   _____

25 Well done, you're the last one out.   _____

5

Move one letter from the first word and add it to the second word to make two new words.

B 13

Example   hunt   sip   <u>hut</u>   <u>snip</u>

26 bear   link   _____   _____

27 plan   fit   _____   _____

28 land   fake   _____   _____

29 done   well   _____   _____

30 stun   peal   _____   _____

5

B 14

Complete the following sentences by selecting the most sensible word from each group of words given in the brackets. Underline the words selected.

Example   The (<u>children</u>, books, foxes) carried the (houses, <u>books</u>, steps) home from the (greengrocer, <u>library</u>, factory).

31 Tim wears a black (shirt, handkerchief, scarf) when he plays (whist, football, scrabble) for the school (journey, team, work).

32 My pencil (grater, sharpener, cutter) is in my (cup, bed, bag) hanging on my (tree, floor, chair).

33 The (car, plane, ship) went into the (house, harbour, shed) very (slowly, cleverly, badly).

34 He (listened, watched, thought) very hard to (hear, catch, throw) the train (floating, going, coming) towards him.

35 In the (Sahara, Antarctic, jungle) icebergs are as (small, old, huge) as (penguins, garages, houses).

5

B 14

Find the missing number by using the two numbers outside the brackets in the same way as the other sets of numbers.

Example   2 [8] 4   3 [18] 6   5 [25] 5

36 11 [23] 12   6 [15] 9   18 [____] 11

37 6 [19] 25   7 [10] 17   9 [____] 23

38 7 [2] 14   11 [3] 33   6 [____] 6

39 3 [30] 5   7 [42] 3   6 [____] 2

40 8 [24] 3   6 [30] 5   9 [____] 8

5

Fill in the crosswords so that all the given words are included. You have been given one letter as a clue in each crossword.

41

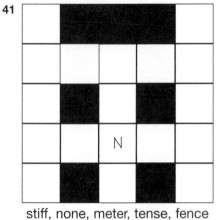

stiff, none, meter, tense, fence

42

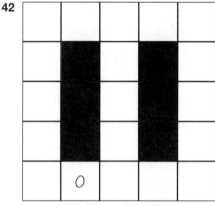

timer, torch, reach, treat, motor

43

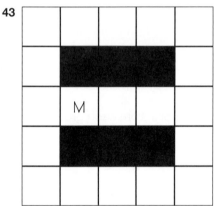

amble, horse, erect, heaps, sport

44

funny, layer, laser, towel, wands

45

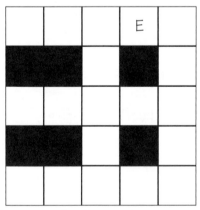

hover, nasty, steam, views, rummy

5

Rearrange the letters in capitals to make another word. The new word has something to do with the first two words.

Example   spot   soil   SAINT   STAIN

46 rock   pebble   NOTES   _____

47	challenge	attempt	DEAR	_____
48	bush	plant	BRUSH	_____
49	box	container	TRACE	_____
50	end	back	RARE	_____

5

51 If 2124 stands for PIPE, 214 stands for _____.

B 24

52 If 2867 stands for LINK, 786 stands for _____.

53 If 5234 stands for WEAR, 342 stands for _____.

54 If 3216 stands for WRAP, 613 stands for _____.

55 If 1729 stands for COAT, 219 stands for _____.

5

If these words were placed in alphabetical order, which word would come fourth?

B 20

56	lounge	locket	locals	loaded	lonely	_____
57	marry	blank	every	blown	march	_____

If these words were listed in reverse alphabetical order, which word would come second?

58	racket	raisin	raffle	rattle	rascal	_____
59	splint	spoken	square	superb	spread	_____
60	concert	foreign	collect	purpose	puppets	_____

5

61–65 Six families live in South Street. From the information below, work out which family lives in which house and write them in on the chart.

B 25

Browns _____   _____   _____

1		3		5

SOUTH STREET

2		4		6

_____   _____   _____

The Greys live between the Blacks and the Whites on the even side on South Street.

The Greens live opposite the Blacks.

The Browns live in Number 1.

The Blues live in a house with a higher number than the Whites.

5

Now go to the Progress Chart to record your score!   Total   65

33

Paper 10

Underline the two words, one from each group, which are closest in meaning. B 3

    Example (race, shop, <u>start</u>) (finish, <u>begin</u>, end)

1 (choose, time, bend)   (trick, open, curve)

2 (big, heavy, small)   (old, slight, alike)

3 (create, ruin, ignore)   (invite, call, destroy)

4 (author, book, story)   (easel, painter, writer)

5 (run, travel, fast)   (slow, carry, swift)

5

Find the three-letter word which can be added to the letters in capitals to make a new word. The new word will complete the sentence sensibly. B 22

    Example The cat sprang onto the MO. <u>USE</u>

6 We plant CABES in our vegetable garden each year. _____

7 The HST boy returned the wallet he found on the road. _____

8 'Take out some PR and a pencil,' said the teacher. _____

9 I like to have lettuce and TOOES in my salad. _____

10 My mum makes me hot tea with lemon when I have a sore THR. _____

5

Underline the one word which **can be made** from the letters of the word in capitals. B 7

    Example CHAMPION camping notch peach cramp <u>chimp</u>

11 HEAVE	head	have	vast	hive	hovel
12 BROTHER	another	there	broke	throb	bribe
13 FORCE	care	forge	core	fudge	free
14 GROPE	grape	rope	grip	rogue	pear
15 HANDS	shape	shore	ship	shade	sand

5

Write the four-letter word hidden at the end of one word and the beginning of the next word. The order of the letters may not be changed. B 21

    Example The children had bats and balls. *sand*

16 I don't like the clothes in this shop. _____

17 The cinema shows new films each week. _____

18 Running around helps tire you out. _____

19 There's been an accident; come at once! _____

20 Jade received letters from people she had never heard of. _____

5

Move one letter from the first word and add it to the second word to make two new words. B 13

Example   hunt   sip   hut   snip

21   fear   can   _____   _____

22   spoil   eat   _____   _____

23   hoist   pant   _____   _____

24   haunt   lid   _____   _____

25   drear   spot   _____   _____

5

Complete the following sentences by selecting the most sensible word from each group of words given in the brackets. Underline the words selected. B 14

Example   The (children, books, foxes) carried the (houses, books, steps) home from the (greengrocer, library, factory).

26   Jane has to go to the (house, cinema, school) as she has an (silly, important, small) exam and she (fears, hopes, wonders) if she will do well.

27   Luckily she (ate, found, read) her (umbrella, book, lunch) just before the (day, rain, bus) began.

28   In the event of a (silence, fire, flood) leave the (street, car, building) (slowly, badly, quickly).

29   I have lost my (ball, book, cat). She is (lazy, black, green) and has a (mouse, paw, collar).

30   He (ate, lost, drank) the lemonade quickly, (put on, took off, bought) his coat and (swam, ran, left).

5

Find and underline the two words which need to change places for the sentence to make sense. B 17

Example   She went to letter the write.

31   The better is weather now.

32   I'm supper forward to looking.

33   I like me book you gave the.

34   Up try to clean it do.

35   I vase over the knocked.

5

Fill in the missing letters and numbers. B 23

Example   AB is to CD as PQ is to RS.

36   A82 is to B81 as C80 is to _____.

37   D19 is to E19 as F20 is to _____.

38   C9 is to D12 as E15 is to _____.

39   AB5 is to CD6 as EF7 is to _____.

40   KLM is to MNO as OPQ is to _____.

5

Underline the two words, one from each group, which are most opposite in meaning.

B 9

Example (dawn, early, wake) (late, stop, sunrise)

41 (still, quiet, sudden) (motionless, active, silence)

42 (icy, freezing, warm) (cool, cold, frosty)

43 (bend, loosen, crack) (straighten, drop, catch)

44 (fix, trade, sell) (destroy, repair, improve)

45 (inside, low, between) (under, high, below)

5

Write these words backwards and put them in alphabetical order.

B 20

GAMBIT   GARLAND   GALLOP   GAMBLE   GATHER

_____   _____   _____   _____   _____

46 Which is now the first word? _____

47 Which is now the middle word? _____

48 Which two letters are in all the words? _____

49 When the word is written forwards, which word
has all the letters after the first in alphabetical order? _____

50 What is the total number of As in the words? ____

5

If the code for DETAINS is ghbjklm, what are the codes for the following words?

B 24

51 NEAT   52 DENT

_____   _____

What do these codes stand for?

53 ghjl   54 mbjkl

_____   _____

4

Choose the word or phrase that makes the sentence true.

B 14

Example A LIBRARY always has (posters, a carpet, books, DVDs, stairs).

55 A PARTY always has (cake, music, gifts, guests, games).

56 A DOG always has a (lead, collar, kennel, tag, coat).

57 A RESTAURANT always has (food, a patio, music, tablecloths, candles).

58 A CAR always has (passengers, air conditioning, a radio, a clock, a steering
wheel).

59 A BOARD GAME always has (dice, rules, cards, a timer, a scorecard).

5

36

Choose two words, one from each set of brackets, to complete the sentence in the best way.

B 15

Example Tall is to (tree, <u>short</u>, colour) as narrow is to (thin, white, <u>wide</u>).

60 Combine is to (leave, destroy, add) as subtract is to (cover, move, reduce).

61 Fail is to (lose, try, play) as draw is to (tie, improve, succeed).

62 Trap is to (catch, deliver, ignore) as release is to (free, lose, protect).

63 Donate is to (charge, win, give) as receive is to (accept, present, sell).

64 Order is to (choose, command, use) as ask is to (answer, request, refuse).

65 Erase is to (delete, highlight, insert) as ring is to (circle, finger, hoop).

6

Now go to the Progress Chart to record your score!   Total   **65**

Paper 11

Underline the two words in each line which are most similar in type or meaning.

B 5

Example <u>dear</u> pleasant poor extravagant <u>expensive</u>

1 hot	cold	shout	wet	yell
2 go	frighten	need	calm	require
3 bench	tape	parcel	mail	chair
4 show	light	ask	day	enquire
5 open	stand	close	sit	shut

5

Find the three-letter word which can be added to the letters in capitals to make a new word. The new word will complete the sentence sensibly.

B 22

Example The cat sprang onto the MO. U<u>SE</u>

6 He bought an EXSIVE car.   _____

7 The cup SMED on the floor.   _____

8 Next month will be MH.   _____

9 The car was driven BACKDS.   _____

10 He SPED on the icy road.   _____

5

If the letters in the following words were arranged in alphabetical order, which letter would come in the middle?

B 20

11 baron ____   12 night ____

13 earth ____   14 youth ____

15 torch ____

5

Find a word that can be put in front of each of the following words to make new, compound words.

Example   cast   fall   ward   pour   _down_

16 storm	ball	plough	man	_____
17 out	book	cuff	shake	_____
18 fall	proof	tight	colour	_____
19 ground	line	stand	arm	_____
20 where	one	time	how	_____

 5

Write the four-letter word hidden at the end of one word and the beginning of the next word. The order of the letters may not be changed.

Example   The children had bats and balls.   _sand_

21 The approach to the school is busy.   _____

22 Each pair is different.   _____

23 He started school when he was five years old.   _____

24 There was no need for you to cry.   _____

25 It is nice when we are here on time.   _____

 5

Change the first word into the last word by changing one letter at a time and making a new, different word in the middle.

Example   CASE   _CASH_   LASH

26 STAY   _____   SLAM

27 THAT   _____   CHAP

28 CAST   _____   PASS

29 FIRE   _____   DIRT

30 DUCK   _____   LACK

 5

Find and underline the two words which need to change places for the sentence to make sense.

Example   She went to <u>letter</u> the <u>write</u>.

31 New is your which house?

32 The wet is awfully towel.

33 Do borrow want to you it?

34 She very it was said interesting.

35 I cover the picture on the like.

Change one word so that the sentence makes sense. Underline the word you are taking out and write your new word on the line.

Example   I waited in line to buy a <u>book</u> to see the film.   _ticket_

36 The alphabet has 26 different numbers.   _____

37 A torch can help you see in the light.   _____

38 An aeroplane can run to other countries.   _____

39 Using a skipping string can keep you fit.   _____

40 Peas, beans and carrots are all flowers.   _____

Fill in the crosswords so that all the given words are included. You have been given one letter as a clue in each crossword.

41
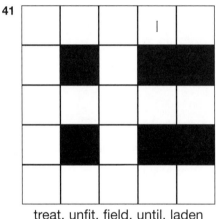

treat, unfit, field, until, laden

42
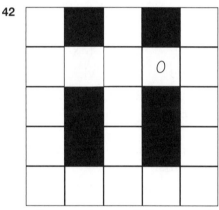

allow, parks, spell, flake, swell

43
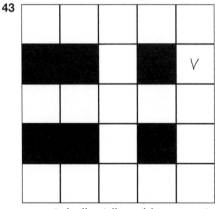

great, ladle, tribe, drive, event

44
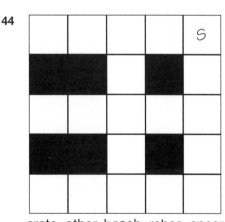

crate, other, beach, robes, spear

45

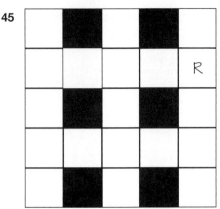

ankle, super, usual, spoke, creek

5

Give the two missing groups of letters and numbers in the following sequences. The alphabet has been written out to help you.

B 23

A B C D E F G H I J K L M N O P Q R S T U V W X Y Z

Example CQ   DP   EQ   FP   *GQ*   *HP*

46 BK   BL   CM   ___   ___   DP

47 2P   ___   8T   11V   14X   ___

48 ___   YB   XC   ___   VE   UF

49 WV   XT   ___   ZP   ___   BL

50 DCB   EDC   FED   ___   ___   IHG

5

Rearrange the letters in capitals to make another word. The new word has something to do with the first two words.

B 16

Example spot   soil   SAINT   *STAIN*

51 cut   rip   RATE   _____

52 nuisance   annoyance   PETS   _____

53 food   dinner   MALE   _____

54 pipe   tube   SHOE   _____

55 whiskers   moustache   BREAD   _____

5

If a = 2, b = 3, c = 4, d = 5, f = 6, g = 7, find the answer to the following calculations.

B 26

56 abc = ___   **57** bcd = ___

2

Solve the problems by working out the letter codes. The alphabet has been written out to help you.

B 24

A B C D E F G H I J K L M N O P Q R S T U V W X Y Z

Example In a code, SECOND is written as UGEQPF. How would you write THIRD?
        VJKTF

58 In a code, FLOWER is written as DJMUCP. How would you write LOW? _____

59 In a code, RUN is written as TWP. What does mean PWV mean?   _____

60 In a code, JUMP is written as ITLO. What does ETM mean? _____

61 In a code, DUCK is written as CTBJ. How would you write NEXT? _____

62 In a code, ROSE is written as SPTF. How would you write HOLIDAY? _____ ◯ 5

Find a word that is similar in meaning to the word in capital letters and that rhymes with the second word. B 5

    Example   CABLE   tyre   _wire_

63 GROUP   stand   _____

64 UNEVEN   cuff   _____

65 NOT SOUR   bleat   _____   ◯ 3

**Now go to the Progress Chart to record your score!**   **Total** ◯ 65

Paper 12

Underline the two words which are the odd ones out in the following groups of words. B 4

    Example   black   <u>king</u>   purple   green   <u>house</u>

1 skip	lead	walk	run	iron
2 river	mountain	ocean	sea	hill
3 cross	kind	generous	angry	loving
4 red	sun	blue	moon	green
5 sunny	rest	warm	sleep	fine

◯ 5

Find the three-letter word which can be added to the letters in capitals to make a new word. The new word will complete the sentence sensibly. B 22

    Example   The cat sprang onto the MO.   _USE_

6 It was so cold it was SING.   _____

7 The king shouted for his SERT.   _____

8 He woke LY that morning.   _____

9 She picked some PROSES in the wood.   _____

10 The dog gave him a nasty SCCH.   _____   ◯ 5

Underline two words, one from each group, that go together to form a new word. The word in the first group always comes first.

Example (hand, <u>green</u>, for)   (light, <u>house</u>, sure)

11 (red, green, blue)   (fingers, bell, rose)

12 (sun, light, bright)   (rub, off, shine)

13 (short, tall, foot)   (step, sure, arm)

14 (now, after, before)   (wards, went, down)

15 (short, foot, hurt)   (good, goal, ball)

Write the four-letter word hidden at the end of one word and the beginning of the next word. The order of the letters may not be changed.

Example   The children had bats and balls.   _sand_

16 My mother makes us keep our house tidy.   _____

17 I like juice made from tropical fruits.   _____

18 Each apple costs forty-nine pence.   _____

19 After all those years, I was still interested in it.   _____

20 Despite losing I don't regret changing.   _____

Move one letter from the first word and add it to the second word to make two new words.

Example   hunt sip   _hut_   _snip_

21 steam   key   _____   _____

22 float   her   _____   _____

23 stall   kin   _____   _____

24 bread   foe   _____   _____

25 print   ate   _____   _____

Complete the following sentences by selecting the most sensible word from each group of words given in the brackets. Underline the words selected.

Example   The (<u>children</u>, books, foxes) carried the (houses, <u>books</u>, steps) home from the (greengrocer, <u>library</u>, factory).

26 She (tried, worked, walked) to get her (son, dog, daughter) to do his (radio, drink, homework).

27 The (number, letter, sign) at the end of the (road, word, sum) says (come, run, stop).

28 The (ship, plane, car) in the (lane, sea, sky) is (driving, flying, sailing) very high.

29 We (swum, walked, skipped) as (slowly, lazily, fast) as we could to get to the (castle, cloud, friend) before dark.

30 The (police, villagers, highwaymen) stopped the (canoe, cart, coach) and stole the travellers' (food, shoes, gold).

42

Fill in the missing letters. The alphabet has been written out to help you.

A B C D E F G H I J K L M N O P Q R S T U V W X Y Z

Example   AB is to CD as PQ is to R𝒮.

31 AC is to EG as JL is to _____ .

32 AB is to WX as CD is to _____ .

33 ACE is to BDF as LNP is to _____ .

34 AZ is to BY as CX is to _____ .

35 ACB is to BCA as EGF is to _____ .

Fill in the crosswords so that all the given words are included. You have been given one letter as a clue in each crossword.

36

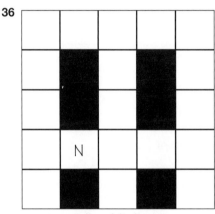

anvil, orbit, brave,
tails, organ

37

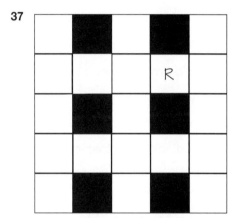

ochre, least, chest,
ports, tusks

38

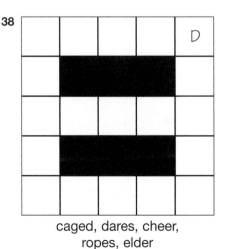

caged, dares, cheer,
ropes, elder

39

punch, sighs, husks,
sates, night

40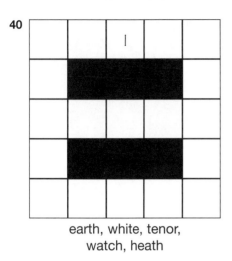

earth, white, tenor,
watch, heath

Change one word so that the sentence makes sense. Underline the word you are taking out and write your new word on the line.

B 14

      Example   I waited in line to buy a <u>book</u> to see the film.   *ticket*

41 If you don't eat fish or fruit you are a vegetarian.   _____

42 In a car you should always draw a seat belt.   _____

43 In Chinese restaurants many people read with chopsticks.   _____

44 Noughts and stars is a fun game to play with friends.   _____

45 It was so hot last night that a tree in our garden was blown over.   _____

5

Here are the number codes for four words. Match the right word to the right code.

B 24

    S H O E   S O W   R O S E   W H O S E   S H O W

    5 7 6 2   5 7 6 1   2 7 6 5 1   8 6 5 1   5 6 2

46 SHOE _____   **47** WHOSE _____

48 SOW _____   **49** SHOW _____

50 ROSE _____

5

Choose two words, one from each set of brackets, to complete the sentences in the best way.

B 15

      Example   Tall is to (tree, <u>short</u>, colour) as narrow is to (thin, white, <u>wide</u>).

51 Dusk is to (evening, dark, moon) as dawn is to (sunset, night, morning).

52 Common is to (few, ordinary, lost) as unique is to (unusual, broken, expensive).

53 Sudden is to (skilled, quiet, swift) as gradual is to (steady, new, careless).

54 Leaning is to (tilted, standing, thin) as upright is to (straight, fallen, lying).

55 Horse is to (ride, saddle, hoof) as dog is to (bone, walk, pet).

5

If a = 2, b = 3, c = 4, d = 5, find the answer to the following calculations.

B 26

56 a + b + c = _____

57 (c + d) ÷ b = _____

2

Find the letter which will complete both pairs of words, ending the first word and starting the second. The same letter must be used for both pairs of words.

B 10

Example   mea (t) able   fi (t) ub

58 man (___) awn   da (___) et

59 tra (___) ea   ho (___) it

60 daw (___) ote   mai (___) un

61 pas (___) aw   wa (___) ty

62 bea (___) ry   be (___) ew

5

Find a word that is similar in meaning to the word in capital letters and that rhymes with the second word.

B 5

Example   CABLE   tyre   *wire*

63 A FISH   spout   _____

64 HOUSE   comb   _____

65 FOG   hissed   _____

Now go to the Progress Chart to record your score!   Total   65

Paper 13

1–5 Look at these groups of words.

B 1

A	B	C	D
mule	theatre	spanner	purple
monkey	town hall	anvil	pink

Choose the correct group for each of the words below. Write in the letter.

bridge ___   drill ___   ferret ___   baboon ___

arcade ___   rose ___   cinema ___   beige ___

mole ___   saw ___

5

45

Underline the two words, one from each group, which are the most opposite in meaning.

B 9

Example   (dawn, <u>early</u>, wake)   (<u>late</u>, stop, sunrise)

6 (break, whole, part)   (mend, fast, heal)

7 (long, land, stretch)   (length, measure, shrink)

8 (heat, empty, weight)   (bottom, full, light)

9 (lost, frighten, plentiful)   (lots, scarce, scare)

10 (fight, top, winner)   (left, loser, first)

5

Find the letter which will end the first word and start the second word.

B 10

Example   peac (<u>h</u>) ome

11 num (___) read   12 pip (___) ver   13 tos (___) oak

14 pla (___) ell   15 tha (___) int

5

Underline the one word which **cannot be made** from the letters of the word in capital letters.

B 7

Example   STATIONERY   stone   tyres   ration   <u>nation</u>   noisy

16 TERRACE   care   rate   stain   trace   crate

17 DISTANT   stead   stand   stint   ants   dint

18 PAINTER   trip   rain   tramp   nape   print

19 GENERAL   large   near   rage   gear   ages

20 CLEAREST   clean   real   star   race   steer

5

Write the four-letter word hidden at the end of one word and the beginning of the next word. The order of the letters may not be changed.

B 21

Example   The children had bats and balls.   <u>sand</u>

21 Going to the seaside is an ideal tonic.   _____

22 The cup is beside a bunch of flowers.   _____

23 Her teeth are white and beautifully clean.   _____

24 It means it is easy to control.   _____

25 We think that our ways are best.   _____

5

Change the first word into the last word by changing one letter at a time and making a new, different word in the middle.

B 13

Example   CASE   *CASH*   LASH

26 GEAR _____ HEAL   27 FIRM _____ HARM

28 BULB _____ SULK   29 WISE _____ WANE

30 SEAT _____ SEND

5

Complete the following sentences by selecting the most sensible word from each group of words given in the brackets. Underline the words selected.

B 14

Example The (<u>children</u>, books, foxes) carried the (houses, <u>books</u>, steps) home from the (greengrocer, <u>library</u>, factory).

31 The day was (frosty, sunny, raining) and the (dog, woman, baby) went to sunbathe at the (town, slopes, beach).

32 It was (spring, summer, autumn), the trees were (brown, dead, green) and the (toads, birds, lambs) were in the fields.

33 We ran (yesterday, tomorrow, quickly) to the (house, shop, station) as we didn't want to miss the (truck, bike, train).

34 The (wheelbarrow, boat, tree) hit the (rock, grass, rain) so hard that (water, ice, birds) came on board.

35 We (ran, walked, jumped) overboard. The water was (dirty, muddy, cold) but we warmed up as we (drank, swam, ate).

Underline the one word in the brackets which will go equally well with both the pairs of words outside the brackets.

B 5

Example rush, attack   cost, fee   (price, hasten, strike, <u>charge</u>, money)

36 untruth, false   rest, lounge   (sleep, invent, fall, lie, support)

37 group, gang   fill, box   (tie, luggage, pack, carry, crate)

38 planet, sun   performer, celebrity   (moon, sky, actor, hero, star)

39 considerate, nice   type, sort   (gentle, kind, set, class, friendly)

40 cool, chilly   flu, infection   (freezing, sneeze, illness, cold, icy)

Fill in the crosswords so that all the given words are included. You have been given one letter as a clue in each crossword.

B 19

41
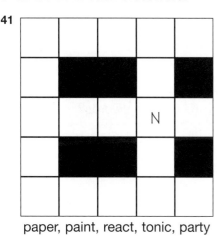

paper, paint, react, tonic, party

42
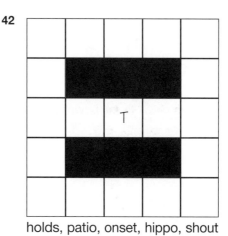

holds, patio, onset, hippo, shout

47

43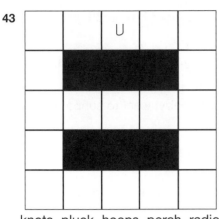

knots, pluck, hoops, perch, radio

44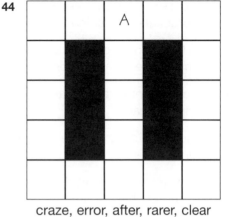

craze, error, after, rarer, clear

45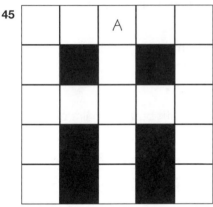

alter, brave, bison, easel, sites

Give the two missing groups of letters and numbers in the following sequences.
The alphabet has been written out to help you.

A B C D E F G H I J K L M N O P Q R S T U V W X Y Z

Example	CQ	DP	EQ	FP	<u>GQ</u>	<u>HP</u>

46 ___   EQ   FR   DS   ET   ___

47 128J   64L   32N   16P   ___   ___

48 AA   BA   ___   DB   EC   ___

49 8C   5B   ___   ___   8Y   5X

50 ___   ___   DW   CX   BY   AZ

If the code for GRATE is △ ○ ◆ 99 ①, what are the codes for the following words?

51 RATE _____   **52** EAR _____

What do these codes stand for?

53 99 ◆ △   _____

54 99 ① ◆   _____

55 △ ○ ① ◆ 99   _____

5

B 23

5

B 24

5

The first 10 letters of the alphabet are written as the first 10 numbers, i.e. A = 1 B = 2 etc. B 24

Write these as numbers.

56 HIDE _____   **57** CAGED _____

What are these words?

58 61354 _____   **59** 854754 _____   **60** 25138 _____   5

Underline the word in each line that has its letters in alphabetical order.   B 20

61 word   act   letter   seen   frog

62 omelette   gasp   belt   through   under

63 know   gain   team   soon   from

64 spoon   pram   night   brag   moor

65 slice   peach   dunk   sty   frail   5

Now go to the Progress Chart to record your score!   **Total** 65

Paper 14

Underline the pair of words most similar in meaning.   B 5

   Example   come, go   roam, wander   fear, fare

  1 appreciation, thanks   please, prize   gale, calm

  2 present, past   paper, bins   creak, squeak

  3 unknown, famous   gallant, brave   soap, brush

  4 rubbish, litter   noun, verb   noisy, quiet

  5 hour, time   silence, quietness   dust, polish   5

Find the letter which will end the first word and start the second word.   B 10

   Example   peac (h) ome

  6 whe (___) ettle   **7** fea (___) ubber

  8 swor (___) elight   **9** ste (___) ount

 10 soun (___) awn   5

Underline one word in the brackets which is most opposite in meaning to the word in capitals.   B 6

   Example   WIDE   (broad   vague   long   narrow   motorway)

 11 ODD   (peculiar   queer   strange   even   unjust)

 12 SHALLOW   (deep   water   dive   puddle   shape)

49

13 WHOLE   (complete   part   some   never   here)

14 SAD   (miserable   joyful   sorry   hopeless   hateful)

15 START   (begin   open   commence   end   first)

5

Look at the first group of three words. The word in the middle has been made from the other two words. Complete the second group of three words in the same way, making a new word in the middle.

B 18

    Example   PAIN   INTO   TOOK   ALSO   <u>SOON</u>   ONLY

16 COMB   BALE   ALES   PART   _____   RAPS

17 WIDE   DESK   SKIP   SITE   _____   AMPS

18 OPEN   NOSE   SENT   RAID   _____   AGUE

19 SAGE   GETS   TEST   MAST   _____   TONE

20 FREE   REEL   SEAL   SPOT   _____   FRET

5

Underline two words, one from each group, that go together to form a new word. The word in the first group always comes first.

B 8

    Example   (hand, <u>green</u>, for)   (light, <u>house</u>, sure)

21 (no, two, duet)   (end, here, thing)

22 (drive, steer, car)   (hat, road, pet)

23 (land, earth, sky)   (mark, road, way)

24 (how, an, why)   (self, other, is)

25 (cot, bed, sleep)   (stead, stroll, stand)

5

Write the four-letter word hidden at the end of one word and the beginning of the next word. The order of the letters may not be changed.

B 21

    Example   The children had bats and balls.   <u>sand</u>

26 A single apple is very good for you.   _____

27 This kind of behaviour is useless.   _____

28 To speak like that isn't allowed.   _____

29 You will need to write that far more neatly.   _____

30 Come quickly or you will be too late.   _____

5

Change the first word into the last word by changing one letter at a time and making a new, different word in the middle.

B 13

    Example   CASE   <u>CASH</u>   LASH

31 FAKE   _____   BALE

32 LARK   _____   MARE

33 MADE ———— CAKE

34 SONG ———— LONE

35 COLD ———— COOT ⟲ 5

Find and underline the two words which need to change places for the sentence to make sense.

Example She went to <u>letter</u> the <u>write</u>.

36 Do borrow want to you it?

37 Where shoes your are?

38 I must one a new buy.

39 It clean I'll tomorrow.

40 I full I'll get hope marks. ⟲ 5

Choose two words, one from each set of brackets, to complete the sentence in the best way.

Example Smile is to happiness as (drink, <u>tear</u>, shout) is to (whisper, laugh, <u>sorrow</u>).

41 Depart is to leave as (change, ignore, finish) is to (remain, begin, conclude).

42 Heat is to warm as (wash, freeze, chop) is to (cool, boil, bake).

43 Pence is to pound as (second, day, month) is to (minute, century, decade).

44 Find is to lose as (easy, earth, ebb) is to (sun, flow, world).

45 Midnight is to night as (evening, noon, night) is to (day, dawn, winter). ⟲ 5

Choose the word or phrase that makes the sentence true.

Example A LIBRARY always has (posters, a carpet, <u>books</u>, DVDs, stairs).

46 A BANK always has (sweets, music, coffee, money, a guard).

47 A CAMERA always has (film, a strap, a case, a lens, a stand).

48 A PIANO always has (keys, music, a music stand, a seat, a clock).

49 A CHAIR always has (wheels, arms, a cushion, a seat, a footrest).

50 A FATHER always has a (wife, hobby, child, car, daughter). ⟲ 5

If the code for AVERAGE is ◆ 99 ○ ① ◆ △ ○, what are the codes for the following words?

51 VEER ————   52 REAR ————

What do these codes stand for?

53 △ ○ ◆ ① ————   54 ○ ◆ △ ○ ① ————

55 △ ◆ 99 ○ ————   ⟲ 5

(51)

If A = 1, B = 2, C = 3, D = 4, E = 5, F = 6, find the sum of these words.

B 26

56 F + E + E + D = ___   **57** C + A + F + E = ___

58 B + E + A + D = ___   **59** F + A + C + E = ___

60 D + E + A +F = ___

5

Five children did a test for which 100 marks were awarded. R lost 4 marks, M had half as many marks as the person who came top, G lost 5 marks, D had 7 marks fewer than G and S had 12 marks fewer than R.

B 25

61 Who came top? ___   **62** Who was 2nd? ___

63 Who came 3rd? ___   **64** Who came 4th? ___

65 Who came 5th? ___

5

Now go to the Progress Chart to record your score!   **Total**   65

Paper 15

Change one word so that the sentence makes sense. Underline the word you are taking out and write your new word on the line.

B 14

Example   I waited in line to buy a <u>book</u> to see the film.   *ticket*

1 Summer is my favourite season because I love it when it snows.   _____

2 I sent out newspapers to everyone I wanted to come to my birthday party.   _____

3 My mother sings out a story to me before bed each night.   _____

4 The monkey is known as the king of the jungle.   _____

5 Elm, oak and maple are all types of flower.   _____

5

Underline the pair of words most opposite in meaning.

B 9

Example   cup, mug   coffee, milk   <u>hot, cold</u>

6 conceal, hide   front, back   modern, new

7 rough, smooth   rapid, quick   hope, help

8 tested, tried   bent, straight   gap, hole

9 stern, strict   ally, friend   sell, buy

10 here, there   show, display   angry, cross

5

Remove two letters from the word in capital letters to leave a new word. The meaning of the new word is given in the clue.

B 12

Example   MONKEY lives in a monastery   <u>monk</u>

11 HOUSES   tube   _____

12 GRAPES   knocks   _____

13 SWARMS   not cool   _____

14 THINGS   not that   _____

15 SHEATH   chair   _____

5

Find a word that can be put in front of each of the following words to make new, compound words.

B 11

Example   cast   fall   ward   pour   <u>down</u>

16 bow   drop   fall   coat   _____

17 guard   fly   work   place   _____

18 ache   brush   paste   pick   _____

19 show   works   block   worthy   _____

20 struck   beam   light   stone   _____

5

Write the four-letter word hidden at the end of one word and the beginning of the next word. The order of the letters may not be changed.

B 21

Example   The children had bats and balls.   <u>sand</u>

21 For his birthday, I got Dad new socks.   _____

22 The next time he snaps, I'm going!   _____

23 The art teacher was unwell today.   _____

24 She missed her turn due to long queues.   _____

25 Areas of path on the cliff under our feet were slippery.   _____

5

Look at the first group of three words. The word in the middle has been made from the other two words. Complete the second group of three words in the same way, making a new word in the middle of the group.

B 18

Example   PAIN <u>IN</u>TO <u>TO</u>OK   ALSO <u>SOON</u> ONLY

26 CODE   COST   FAST   FROG   _____   GLEE

27 DECK   KICK   SICK   KIND   _____   LEAD

28 OPEN	PETS	POTS	DISK	_____	ABLE
29 CLAP	PLAN	NAPE	CRAB	_____	TASK
30 SLIP	PILL	LOUD	DRAB	_____	KNOW

Find and underline the two words which need to change places for the sentence to make sense.

Example   She went to <u>letter</u> the <u>write</u>.

31 Do Street live on the High you?

32 It is wilting and the flowers are hot.

33 I've paper all the used already.

34 The blissfully slept cat in the sun.

35 I feel in sick a car.

Underline the word in the brackets closest in meaning to the word in capitals.

Example   UNHAPPY (unkind   death   laughter   <u>sad</u>   friendly)

36 REPLY   (question   comment   answer   write   explain)

37 DISCOVER   (lose   hide   lock   borrow   find)

38 EXAMINE   (own   paint   fix   study   trick)

39 TRUST   (win   believe   pay   stop   consider)

40 LONG   (short   small   lengthy   light   thin)

Fill in the crosswords so that all the given words are included. You have been given one letter as a clue in each crossword.

41
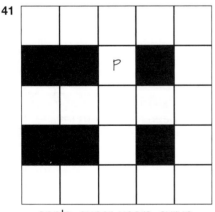

apple, super, years, syrup, bleep

42
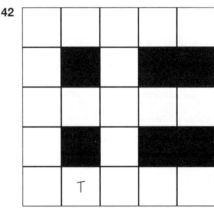

lemon, other, sense, lasso, munch

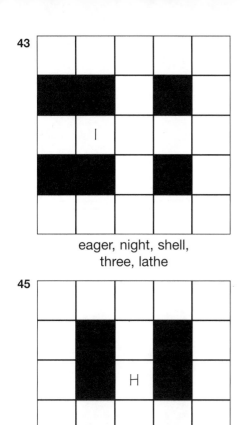

43

eager, night, shell,
three, lathe

44

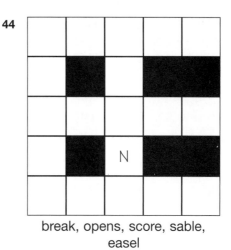

break, opens, score, sable,
easel

45

drear, arena, crowd, other, clear

5

In each line underline the word which would come in the middle if the words were arranged in alphabetical order.

B 20

46 RECKON	REASON	REBEL	READY	REALISE
47 SCHEME	SAILOR	SCENE	SCARED	SAFETY
48 DEPRESS	DELETE	DEPEND	DELIGHT	DELIVER
49 CLOSE	CHASE	CLIFF	CHAOS	CHART
50 BOILING	BRAWL	BLANK	BOAST	BLARE

5

Here are the codes for five words. Match the right word to the right code.

B 24

C H A R T	C H E A P	P E A R	P A R T	R E A C H
△ 4 3 0	△ 3 0 7	0 4 3 1 ✦	1 ✦ 4 3 △	1 ✦ 3 0 7

51 CHART _____   **52** CHEAP _____

53 PEAR _____   **54** PART _____

55 REACH _____

5

(55)

Find the letter which will complete both pairs of words, ending the first word and starting the second. The same letter must be used for both pairs of words.

Example mea (t) able   fi (t) ub

56 drin (___) now   flic (___) ite

57 stu (___) un   fla (___) at

58 til (___) yes   slim (___) nds

59 wor (___) ose   pla (___) ewt

60 mea (___) ight   fil (___) ost

5

Add one letter to the word in capital letters to make a new word. The meaning of the new word is given in the clue.

B 12

Example   PLAN   simple   plain

61 ARE   not covered   _____

62 MAN   most important   _____

63 RAT   a float   _____

64 OVER   put on top of   _____

65 SORT   little   _____

5

Now go to the Progress Chart to record your score!   **Total**   65

Progress Chart   Verbal Reasoning 9–10 years Book 1

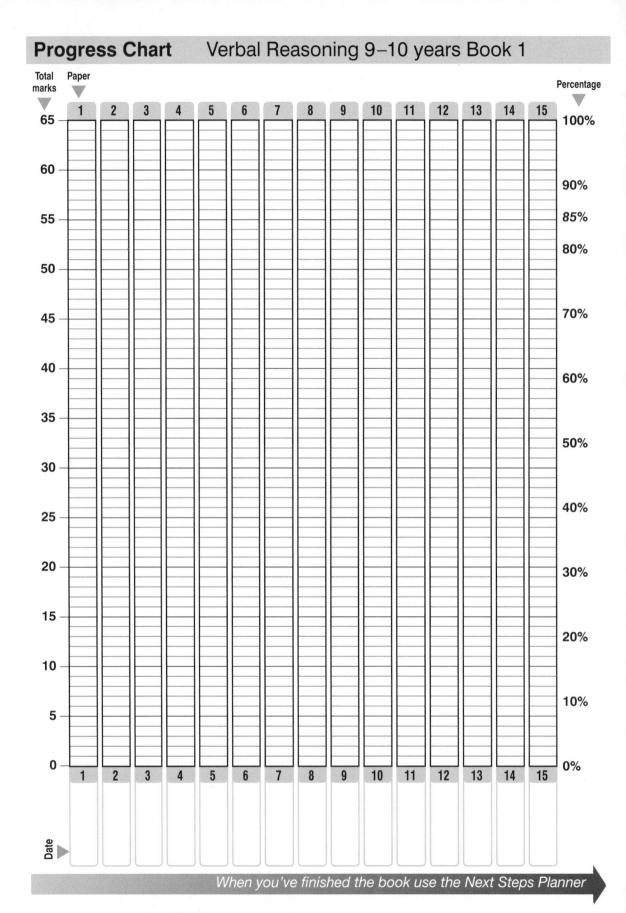

Total marks

Paper

Percentage

| Paper | 1 | 2 | 3 | 4 | 5 | 6 | 7 | 8 | 9 | 10 | 11 | 12 | 13 | 14 | 15 |

65 — 100%

60 — 90%

55 — 85%
80%

50

45 — 70%

40 — 60%

35 — 50%

30

25 — 40%

20 — 30%

15 — 20%

10

5 — 10%

0 — 0%

Date ▶

When you've finished the book use the Next Steps Planner ➤